ISLAM AND THE ENVIRONMENTAL CRISIS

Akhtaruddin Ahmad
M.A., LL.B., Barrister-at Law

with

Dr. Majid H.A. Hashim
Chairman, Environmental Science Dept.
King Abdul Aziz University, Jeddah

and

Dr. Ghazi Al Hachim, Environmental Science Dept.
King Abdul Aziz University, Jeddah

Ta-Ha Publishers Ltd.
1 Wynne Road
London SW9 0BB
United Kingdom

Copyright © Ta-Ha Publishers Ltd. 1997

Published in Rabiʿ al-Awwal 1417 AH/Sept. 1997 CE by

Ta-Ha Publishers Ltd.
1 Wynne Road
London SW9 0BB
website:http://www.taha.co.uk/
email: sale@taha.co.uk

All rights reserved. No part of this publication may be reproduced, stored in any retrieval system, or transmitted in any form or by any means, electronic or otherwise, without written permission of the publishers.

By: Akhtaruddin Ahmad
Edited by: ʿAbdassamad Clarke

LEICESTER LIBRARIES	
Askews & Holts	19-Sep-2012
	£6.00

British Library Cataloguing in
Islam and the Environmental Crisis
1. Ahmad, Akhtaruddin

ISBN 1 897940 66 1

Typeset by: ʿAbdassamad Clarke.
Printed and Bound by- De-Luxe Printers,
London NW10 7NR.
website: http://www.de-luxe.com
email: naresh@aapi.co.uk

Contents

INTRODUCTION

All praise and thanks be to Allah, the Lord of the universe, and peace and blessings be upon the Prophet Muhammad and upon his family members, companions, followers and upon all His prophets.

People in the West are now anticipating their millennium and the beginning of the 21st Christian century. But environmental degradation through human malfeasance came to the notice of scientists and environmentalists very recently, to their great surprise and alarm. It was only with the issue of conservation of forests and species that the awareness first dawned, before they discovered that the balance of the global environment is on the brink of collapse through our own acts. Only about thirty years ago they started realizing that the self-inflicted danger is really turning into a far-reaching global disaster endangering the entire world population, rich and poor. Environmentalists point out today that unless humans take care of their own deeds and misdeeds, an environmental doomsday may not be too far off. We have heard enough of past disasters but this one is very much present in our midst.

Is this a fact or science fiction? The question is crystal

clear but the scientists', ecologists', meteorologists', geologists', thinkers' and philosophers' answers have been far from decisive, until quite recently. During the last thirty years this field has generated a lot of research, publication, discussion and action, both on a regional and on a global basis. Yet public awareness is quite minimal, and responsible shoulders to bear the challenge are few. Those who are trying to control and manage the catastrophe, willingly or unwillingly, are not yet fully motivated, morally and ethically.

Environmental pollution is so widespread today in water, air and land that without urgent attention the disaster may destroy our global existence. To enable us to tackle this catastrophe we have to find out how this was caused, who are responsible for it and how to remedy the situation for the sake of all life on our planet Earth.

Yes, credit goes to those activists who very ardently and vigorously have been working in this much needed field of the study of environmental pollution in the national and international arenas. But the problem is so colossal and pervasive that no partial or purely national remedy can cure or control it. We all must gauge the situation physically, morally and globally and try to resolve it squarely. At first glance, besides the general population all the N.G.O.s, states and the United Nations have a very great and urgent role to play in resolving this environmental crisis. But are we all doing the right things? Are the people who have to be fully aware of the responsibility and to discharge their obligations playing their due role? And are the concerned authorities at local and global levels duly motivated to meet the challenge?

Most of the steps on environment taken so far ignore the vital fact that all things and beings are created, as is the earth and other planets and above all the whole universe. The 'big bang', the 'theory of evolution' and other 'theories' of our existence are problematic, partial and unclear hypotheses only. The unique harmony and order of this existence is firmly established beyond any reasonable doubt, otherwise we could not exist for a split second. Humans can do less harm to themselves by maintaining that preordained cosmic order in their personal and natural life. Awareness of that order is not confined to our material knowledge only. So the teachings imparted by the revelations that the world has been granted cannot and should not be kept out of active human consideration. That is why a simultaneous assessment of the live world faiths is imperative for their followers in this environmental crisis.

A vast majority of the world population belongs to the so-called 'monotheistic' religions of Judaism, Christianity and Islam. We placed that word in parentheses because it is a Judaeo-Christian concept very different from our understanding of tawhid. Followers of Zoroastrianism, Buddhism, Hinduism, Sikhism and other religions are also numerous. So it is very important for environmentalists to assess their thoughts pragmatically and motivate the masses and the authorities not only from an egocentric material angle of science and technology but more importantly to moral and ethical objectives. But can or should they ignore science and technology?

So while we discuss the various aspects of the disaster, we can find out if or how the revelations man has received guide their followers or mankind on environmental issues. Many of us are not even aware that some religions, in as much as they retain anything of their original Divine revelation, and thus especially Islam, lay down a proper balanced environmental guidance for mankind to heed, both from moral and scientific angles. We will examine Islam's teaching on that here. We will also examine the message of other religions, if any, on this subject.

A friend of mine rightly asked me why I was interfering in this scientific subject being a lawyer. My honest answer was that it is Allah's benevolence that I should explore the field of the law of the laws, the supreme law, which controls the universe including our planet earth not just materially but ethically and spiritually too. Science needs just, legal and ethical guidance today, without which scientists may reach, and may well already have reached, a point of no return. We, Muslims and non-Muslims, should not be the silent spectators of ethical and legal erosion in this catastrophe. And no one can claim to be a good lawyer or a good scientist who lacks the knowledge of this Supreme Law and of the Law Giver or dares to ignore Him. So we all have united in this prime research on environmental degradation on ethical, religious, scientific, legal and socioeconomic grounds. It took us years of research to collect from the growing volume of environmental facts the material needed for this book, especially the update on the important relationship between the deen and the sciences. Nevertheless, we feel that more can be done without any bias or acrimony. The subject of study can be useful for students, teachers, activists, researchers and administrators worldwide, so any fair comment is most welcome.

We owe thanks to Allah who enabled us to complete this research and to many friends at home and abroad who helped with their valuable ideas and support, especially those learned brothers of King Abdul Aziz University, Jeddah, the Islamic University, Madinah, the Islamic Foundation for Ecology and Environment, Birmingham, the Audoban Society, Maine, USA, the National Religious Partnership for the Environment, New York, USA, the World Watch Institute, Washington USA and the United Nations Environmental Programme, New York, USA and Nairobi, Kenya.

We owe thankful gratitude to Ta Ha Publishers of London who made this work accessible to a world audience.

May Allah help us all in following His true guidance and awaken us to a peaceful moral conscience in all interrelated fields of the global environment. Let us live and let live; not exploit and destroy.

ENVIRONMENT

1.1 What is Environment?

The earth is green as we see, and so is Paradise we are told.

But some don't care whether the earth is green or scorched. And some don't care whether paradise is gained or lost. Nevertheless, we all care that we live well and happily. To live well and happily we always need a clean and clear environment. Whether we have that or not is the question. Before one can answer that we have to know what precisely the environment is. Environment has been defined and described by thinkers and writers in different ways. But the common dictionary meaning is: "surrounding objects, regions or conditions specially circumstances of live society".[1] The meanings of 'surroundings' have been confined by some to mean physical or material circumstances only, but others have incorporated in it both material and moral aspects of our existence.

Human beings are not alone in existence, rather the whole gamut of things and beings, material and spiritual, is in it. 'Environment' includes all surrounding objects of land, water and air together with the outer space of the universe. These objects are interdependent by the very nature of creation and so cannot be treated in isolation. Scientists call this phenomenon of interdependency 'positive feedback loops'. Muslims see it as an aspect of Allah's *rububiyyah* – His Lordship by which He sustains His creations by and through His creation. It is the whole natural system around us – the land we inhabit, the air we breathe, the water we contain and drink, the sun that heats us, the gases we inhale and exhale, the spaces we travel through, the plants, animals, birds, fish and species we deal with, and our lives and deaths – which are the obvious indicators of this inherent interdependency between man and his environment. The use or misuse of one affects the other whether we notice it immediately or not. Sometimes this failure to notice or acknowledge creates a grave crisis or disaster; that's where we are today!

Most environmentalists have put too much emphasis on the material technological aspects of the present day crisis, ignoring the most vital moral and ethical spectrum. They have made invaluable contributions by their sincere efforts in research, discussion, publication and action, but can a half circle be equal to the full circle? We have to evaluate all aspects of this crisis, its cause, its effects and develop comprehensive guidelines for resolving it.

The environmental crisis has no geographical frontiers. The atomic accident of Chernobyl in Russia not only killed and injured many of the Russian people but affected the health, food, vegetation, animal life, water and plant life of western Europe; rather, much further beyond. Radioactive contamination in foods like milk powder, meat, fruit or vegetables even reached other continents. Similarly, deforestation in Africa, Asia, Europe and America not only adversely affects their own peoples and environments but also the peoples and the climates of other continents. Industrial pollution in Europe and North America has not only not spared their own people from ecological disasters, but has even engulfed the entire global population. Acid rain in Sweden or Denmark is no longer confined within their frontiers but spreading elsewhere in America and Afro-Asia. The oil fires and spills in the Gulf war jeopardize not only the environments of Kuwait and Saudi Arabia but also of many neighbouring countries. The environmental effects of local wars in Vietnam, Angola, Afghanistan, Palestine, Iran, Iraq, Somalia, Bosnia, Chechnya, Haiti, Palestine, Kashmir, Mindanao, Northern Ireland, and others travel far beyond their national frontiers. Nuclear fallout and toxic wastes aren't destroying the environments of their test grounds alone but far beyond as well. Many instances can be cited to confirm that today's environmental crisis is both local and global and thus needs both regional and global handling.

World religions, with worldwide followings, may have an important role to play in this crisis, as may governments, authorities and other national and international institutions and activists. Religions, specially those which have clear guidance on this topic for their followers or mankind, might need due consideration by all environmental activists. What is certain is that Islam, which alone has an authentic global nature, whose Messenger, may Allah bless him and grant him peace, is the Seal of the Messengers who alone was sent as "a mercy for all the worlds" and for all mankind, must be of decisive importance. Physical or material conditions alone cannot decide the prevention of environmental degradation, be it local or global. Good intention, moral dedication and physical perception are the primary sources of power for environmentalists. We have to expand our ethical and spiritual thoughts in juxtaposition with the technological agenda for the vast and fast developing environmental knowledge of today.

Is there a real threat of disaster in the environmental crisis or it is a myth? Scientists, governments and ecologists differ on the extent of the threat and how to handle it. But there is a consensus today on two things. Firstly, the problem did not arise in a day or a decade. Secondly, it was created primarily by humans and need surely to be contained by them.

'Ecology', the English word, is derived from the original Greek 'oikos' meaning a house, a closed environment and the biotic interplay of things and beings. The European and American scientists who covered the nitrogen cycles of the forests, the stability of food chains, pollination systems of plants and flowers, animal and plant species on land and water, population growth and dispersal, and their evolution and extinction, began to call themselves 'ecologists' in the 20th century. Ecology sounds synonymous with environment but it is only a part of it.[2-4]

1.2. What is Pollution?

What these pollution degradation problems are and how they are disasters has to be looked into thoroughly. Once we find out, we have to chart a course for our benefit or else accept our doom. Scientists and economists now say that enough is enough. The developing countries of the South may blame the North for the high degree of pollution of the entire environment by the North's reckless exploitation of the natural resources for developing their own material prosperity. The North may blame the South for their apathy towards the sirens warning of the environmental dangers of an already depleted ozone layer, pollution of water and air, damage to the rainforests, the greenhouse effect and nuclear fall out. But the fact remains that the entire global atmosphere is polluted by incalculable human actions, and it may be beyond repair, both in the North and the South.

It is also held that the industrial revolution of the West is mainly responsible for this environmental catastrophe, and the South is blindly following the North to close the wide gap of development again at the instance of the North. Before we can stop the crime we have to know its gravity and how to control it effectively. Just blaming each other will not solve the problem. That is why global awareness is being tackled at the global level at the auspices of the UNO and its affiliated agencies with the collaboration of specialised agencies and many NGOs (Non-Governmental Organisations) national and global. One's first impulse as a global citizen of an increasingly homogenous world culture is that they must all unite – scientists, environmentalists, economists, lawyers, thinkers and even theologians – but as Muslims, without denying the need for unity we must look deeper into causes, effects and cures. Maybe the vast majority of the global population is not yet aware of the gravity of the environmental disaster but there is a vociferous multitude of environmentally conscious people who are already on the alert. That is why it is all the more necessary to pull all material and moral resources unitedly by all sections of the people of all thoughts and beliefs to enlighten and educate ourselves to see deeper into the realities of the age we inhabit and the causes of this crisis and from there to act in such a way as to contain this disaster surely and effectively; undoubtedly for our own good wherever we are. If we follow that path, we will find very surely that the environmental crisis is part of a wider and deeper disease, which while more difficult of cure, is at least we will be convinced the genuine source of the malaise. A sound diagnosis is a significant advance towards healing.

Many mighty and developed civilisations have disappeared from the face of the earth for not paying heed to the truth and to divine guidance: the ancient civilisations of 'Ad, Thamud, Egypt, Babylon, Rome, Carthage, Athens, Gandhara and China and more recently the British, French, Dutch, Spanish, Italian, Mongol, Persian, Saracen, Mughal, Byzantine, Ottoman, German and Soviet Russian empires. We have to learn from their history and take lessons from them before it is too late. With that perspective in mind we will study and analyse the environmental problems of today.

We also have to find out what is pollution and the extent of the catastrophe arising out of pollution or the damaging effect of human malfeasance on our immediate neighbourhoods and on distant lands or on the atmosphere. Every action has a reaction. So what is the reaction to our treatment of the environment in all its facets on the planet Earth? Is all that is happening around us naturally caused, mere "acts of God" as the insurance companies put it, or are we humans contributing by our ignorance?[5] Before we try to analyse pollution and its disastrous effects on mankind and all forms of life let us in brief find out about the types of pollutants.

1.3 Major Pollutants

There are different kinds of pollutants which can damage the water, land, air and atmosphere. These pollutants can be divided into five major categories:

A. Natural

Some of the world's most lethal pollution comes from untreated human and animal sewage. According to one WHO (World Health Organisation) estimate, dirty water and refuge cause about 4/5 of the world's diseases. They kill about 25 million people of the Third World alone. Natural organisms do break down some biological wastes or sometimes even make them into natural fertiliser, but by our careless overloading of the environmental system, an imbalance is created by these natural pollutants.[6]

Sunshine, a natural gift to the world, can also act as any other pollutant when its reflections and rays are interfered with, disturbed, or care is not taken when dealing with it. Ultraviolet rays (UV) can burn any living beings when it penetrates into the skin, injuring their cells. It may cause skin cancer, other melanomas, blindness, or other debilities, in humans. The ozone layer in the atmosphere acts as a shield to the damaging rays of the sun. Because of the sun's power, some of the ancient generations used to worship it as a god when they fell away from the natural tawhid of the fitrah, and as a relic of that in the Gregorian calendar it still plays a dominant role.

B. Toxic chemicals and gases

Thousands of chemicals are manufactured by man, in the fields of health, agriculture, industry, defence and other developments. Over 50,000 chemicals are on commercial sale today and many more used for offensive weaponry are traded or bartered by the developed countries. The annual arms trade today runs into billions of dollars and the consequential use of these weapons creates havoc in the global environment. These man-made chemicals for civil and military uses combine elements which are rarely found together in nature so they break down into natural elements slowly and build up – like metallic particles – in tissues and in organic matter. They include pesticides like DDT and fire retardants like PCB, PBB, pollutants like asbestos and CFC and gases like carbon dioxide, carbon monoxide, Halon and others.[7]

Chemical hazards reach us in the water, air and soil. These hazards are sometimes not apparently recognized or sometimes hidden maliciously by the manufacturers for their own gain. They are all found to be posing a great threat to the global environment.

Production of CFCs and halon began in the 1930s and ever since these compounds have been in increased use as refrigerants, aerosol propellants, foam, solvents and fire retardants. Their constant use by trade and industry is resulting in a rapid rise in concentrations polluting the atmosphere. In Appendix 1 the estimated global production of CFC is shown from 1950 -1991. The figure today is much higher.

C. Fossil Fuels.

Fossil fuels, like coal, gas and oil, when burned release

a number of poisonous gases which slowly can harm both things and living beings. Smog, acid rain, ozone depletion and the greenhouse effect are caused by these gases when excessively released, thus disturbing the natural balance. These are the main resources of industry and energy production. Transport on land, water and air also use these fuels. The emissions of these gases worldwide are slowly poisoning the environment beyond repair.

D. Minerals.

Some minerals like mercury, zinc, lead and cadmium, when used at random without proper care and caution, can cause serious harm to the environment. Mercury is used mainly in manufacturing pesticides and paper, and can poison fish, milk products and human and animal food. Cadmium is used for metal plating and batteries. Zinc mining and smelting with cadmium wastes can harm the kidneys and lungs, like other chemicals and metals which are regarded as carcinogenic. Cancer today occurs more than ever before. Lead is used by industry in petrol, paint and pipes and its pollution can cause brain damage, especially in children.

Besides the five above-mentioned categories of physical pollutants, the most damaging ones are the corruption and injustice which pervade society locally and globally and which are the real causes of the disaster:

> "Indeed in almost every case of environmental devastation, corruption has played a significant role in deadening the ability of the political system to respond to the early signals of degradation brought to its attention."

Senator Al Gore, Vice President of the United States (1992-), in his book *Earth in the Balance*, further holds:

> "Likewise, the continued tolerance of widespread so-

cial injustice has the same corrosive effect on our ability to contemplate vigorous and sustained initiatives. The promotion of justice and the protection of the environment must go hand in hand in any society, whether in the context of nations' domestic policies or in the design of North-South agreements between the industrial nations and the third world." (pp 278-279)[8]

E. Nuclear

Apart from the massive destruction that nuclear explosions can cause, radioactive damage can travel far and last very long.[9] The dreadful atomic bomb explosions in Hiroshima and Nagasaki, Japan, in 1945 did not end the painful saga there. Nuclear tests, accidents and wastes produced thereafter for fifty years in the USA, USSR, UK, France and China became notoriously common, overloading the global environment. Nuclear bombs are no more physically used, because of their disastrous consequences, but their widespread underground, undersea and overground testing by the Big Five and by developing countries like India, Brazil, South Africa and Israel are loaded with serious environmental dangers. These experiments and even the peaceful use of nuclear power are full of risks: accidents and radioactive fallout as experienced by the USA, Soviet Russia, Western Europe and others. Similarly nuclear wastes are also poisonous and their effect can last for aeons if not disposed of safely, and there is almost no way to dispose of them safely.

1.4. Water Pollution

There are various aspects of the degraded environment which need separate treatment. We can start with water which is the essential component of all living beings in its natural pure form. How this valuable gift of Providence is being polluted and damaged by man to his own detriment is the subject matter for discussion in this chapter.

'Water planet' is truly thy name. The planet Earth is three quarters covered with water (72%); only one quarter is land. 94% of this is the salt water of the seven seas. Only 6% is sweet water in rivers, wetlands, lakes, underground aquifers and glaciers. In terms of cubic metres only 9,000 cubic kilometres are available for the entire global population. This natural balance has existed for millions of years. This points the thinking person to the creation of the universe by the universal, omnipotent Creator who orders this balance. Man and other beings are blessed with the use of this life source but there is no blessing in its misuse.

Available water is not a constant deposit in land or sea. It has a routine cycle of movements in forms of vapour, cloud, rain, hail, snow, ebb and tide. One source of that cycle is the abundance of rain falling from the clouds mainly in the temperate lands and the humid tropics. Rainfall in other geographical areas is lower and more scarce. While rains in tropical monsoon areas are abundant, in non-tropical areas like the Middle East, North Africa, Australia, Central and South Western areas of the USA, the west of south America and in global desert areas, rains are scarce. The rain and snow in some European, Asian and American regions of the northern hemisphere are abundant but not so plentiful as in the tropics.

Consumption of available water is highest in industrial countries both for domestic and commercial purposes. The countries of Europe, Canada, USA, Japan and Russia who have the largest industrial and agricultural infrastructure consume the most water. The more they use the more they waste and pollute. Irrigation is a big source of waste, as the water used does not reach the target plant life so easily. Reservoirs, lakes, rivers and seas also give up a substantial portion to evaporation. Some of the wasted water comes back to its source through rain, river and underground seepage. This natural water cycle, is besieged by human pollution, primarily:

a. Nitrates from widely used chemical fertilizers, and phosphates from pesticides;

b. Acid rain caused by air pollution;

c. Toxic wastes dumped into or percolated into water, fouling the water, viz. sewage outflow, wrong pipes or toxic chemicals or germs used in industry and agriculture. Fossil fuels like oil and tar spilt in water.

One UNEP agency reports that industry and agriculture are the main culprits in developed countries in polluting the water. The developing countries are now joining the bandwagon.[10]

Another report of GEMS (Global Environment Monitoring System), which has 344 monitoring stations worldwide, reports that nitrate levels in European rivers are on average 45 times higher than the less polluted rivers of the East. Pesticide phosphate levels are high in some African and Asian rivers of Tanzania, India and Malaysia. The rivers and lakes in USA and Russia are similarly contaminated by hazardous chemicals and wastes.[11]

Humans use clean water not only for drinking and cooking but also for washing and bathing. Bathing in polluted water in rivers, lakes or sea beaches has caused not only disease but also death. Even poisoning of fish by oil spills, chemical and waste pollution is quite common today in all continents. Oil spills in the seas are now mounting up, as can be seen from the chart in Appendix 2. These spills pollute the water affecting human and aquatic life: fish, birds, mammals, weeds, algae and all species. (See Appendix 2 which shows major oil spills.)

Constructing dams for irrigation or electricity looks superficially beneficial but their adverse ecological effects sometimes outstrip the benefits. The classic examples are found in India, China and Brazil. The loss in the water level at lower elevations, deforestation, tribal and local population dislocation at both ends, and loss of vegetation and agriculture cause irreparable loss in the neighbourhood.

The Farakkah Barrage

In India the Farakkah Barrage, built to increase water supply at upper regions of the river Ganges, has created a disaster by drying up and reducing the water levels of the lower riparian rivers, causing colossal loss in agriculture, fisheries and the waterways of Bangladesh. During the monsoon rains (June-October) when India opens up the barrage gates, Bangladesh is flooded on both banks of the rivers and tributaries of the long winding Ganges. In the dry season (November-May) the rare water is unilaterally withdrawn by the barrage and diverted to Indian lands desertifying the lower reaches of Bangladesh. In the first ten years (1975-1985) the flow in the Ganges has been shortened by 25% in duration and quantity causing floods almost every year during the monsoons and causing drought in summer and winter.[12]

In the dry season, when the Barrage gates divert three quarters of its water flow to Indian lands, the rivers of Bangladesh thirst for water and the situation is further worsened by pushing upstream the salty waters of the sea, desertifying the most fertile lands of 'Sonar Bangla'. According to one estimate, after ten years of Barrage operation the total water level in the Ganges river areas in Bangladesh dropped by 80%, and in tributary areas dropped by 40% and the navigable routes shrank by 25%. In the twenty years of its operation, the situation has drastically jeopardised the environment in the water supply, inland navigation, soil degradation, agricultural production, fish supply and climatic condition of the western Bangladesh.[13-15]

These vital river areas are most likely to shrink further by the end of the 20th century, fully desertifying the western part of densely populated Bangladesh. Besides a colossal drop in agricultural production in this granary of food, fish yields – the main source of protein – have gone down considerably. The production of jute – the golden fibre -- has already diminished and so has monsoon rice cultivation, as they both need deep waters for their growth. The environmental and economic disaster in Bangladesh created by the Farakkah Barrage of India needs serious treatment by the world community before it is too late, as the Bangladeshi people are demanding a just share of the international waters with compensation for their huge losses and damage.

The Ganges-Kobadak irrigation project, constructed to offset the diminishing water supply from the Ganges, has primarily collapsed because of this killer barrage. As a result the average temperature in summer has gone up from 37.5° to 43.5° Celsius and the winter temperature has gone down from 12.5° C to 8.5° C mainly due to loss of surface water and the reduction of moisture content in the soil. Less rainfall is also now being measured in this basin.[12]

According to experts the Farakkah Barrage on the Ganges has crippled the environment, industry and agriculture of Bangladesh both on a short term and a long term basis.[15] According to India's next plan, if the waters of the Brahmaputra and Meghna rivers, to its east, from Nepal and Assam can be diverted, then the noose on her neighbour's neck will be complete. Over 50 million of her 115 million people are located in the Ganges (Padma) basin. India, on the plea of flushing the silt of Calcutta harbour 250 kilometres downstream, diverted more than three quarters of the Ganges main stream water to West Bengal and Bihar. It was actually for her own agricultural prosperity, reducing the people of Bangladesh to utter misery and suffering after its independence. This was said to be one of the prime objects of Indian and Soviet armed aggression in 1971. The unilateral withdrawal of riparian water, against international law, was not possible in the case of Indus water in West Pakistan due to the IBRD mediated water-sharing treaty of 1960. So it suited India and Soviet Russia well to divide Pakistan with direct intervention of their armed forces in 1971. It enabled India to make Bangladesh her market and a vassal state weakening Islamic Pakistan and enriching Soviet Russian influence over 1,100 million people. (See *Nationalism or Islam*)[16]

The bilateral Ganges water agreements of 1975 and 1977 did no good to Bangladesh and the same thing may happen with the 1997 treaty, as they were all dictated by India and rubber-stamped by India's vassal Government in Bangladesh. They did not consider the huge, direct and indirect, environmental and economic, short and long-term impacts on the poorest people of the earth or its global effect.[12]

Dam and deforestation projects in South East Asia, Africa and South America are similarly displacing the original inhabitants and causing other environmental problems there and elsewhere. Some ill-conceived dam and irrigation projects in Russia, India and China have similar or worse ecological effects, which we learn from daily reports. Some irrigation and dam projects supported by the World Bank, e.g. in India and Brazil, have been questioned by environmentalists, not on the grounds of pollution alone but on other serious ecological considerations, e.g. snatching away the rights of hearth and home, and life and liberty of the silenced inhabitants.

Instead of taking a chauvinistic, political, material approach to national goals on water shortage or pollution control, a global understanding is a must. The steps taken for the joint management of North American lakes, European Rhine river, the Nile and Zambezi rivers and Lake Chad of Africa are laudable examples set by some riparian countries. Unilateral national control has been given up in favour of a regional control for the good of all affected people and the environment, unlike Indian unilateral control of the river Ganges in Farakkah. More international protocols are essential in the water management of the common lakes, rivers and seas in different continents; in the legal terms used to control international waters.

Law of the Sea

The UN Convention on the Law of the Sea is a laudable global effort recently passed to protect water and other natural resources in the vast waters of the seven seas. The Convention is already approved by 160 countries but yet to be put into full force legally.

This Covention was adopted after long years of procrastination only in 1982 and was open for signature till December 1984. It took the member countries of the East and West more than ten years to sign and put into effect, evidencing a classic example of lack of seriousness in handling the environmental catastrophe.

The Convention with 320 Articles and nine Annexes incorporated some important provisions on environmental conservation on sea, land and air. Articles 116-120 deal with conservation and management of the live resources of the high seas. It includes all species like fish and mammals but underwater food, plants, weeds and fungus are forgotten.

Articles 204-222 deal with monitoring the risks and effects of pollution with the enforcement of marine pollution regulations. Pollution through sea-bed activities, dumping of materials, operation of vessels and degrading the atmosphere are meant to be controlled, prevented and reduced by national and global regulations which are yet to come into operation. The marine scientific research to cover pollution and its control is dealt with in Articles 238-262.

By the concluding articles the settlement of disputes is taken care of by amicable settlement and, failing which, by an International Tribunal to be based in Hamburg with Authority headquarters in Jamaica. The Convention has gone a long way to tackle some environmental problems but is a long way behind in actual confrontation of the disaster. The ocean waters serve as habitats of a vast array of plants, fishes, minerals and species accounting for vast resources for human consumption. Over 50% of the people of developing countries obtain more than 30% of their protein from marine fish. Huge amounts of gas and oil are drilled from the sea-beds. Plants and species, when carefully developed, can meet a lot of material and aesthetic human needs. But lack of proper management is polluting and damaging these limited water resources forever, causing incredible risks for the increasing population, creating an imbalance in the environment of the entire world. "Water, water everywhere, Nor a drop to drink," the poet Coleridge's *Ancient Mariner* rhyme is true today not for sea water alone, but for the fresh waters of lakes and rivers as well.

As industries and cities mushroom they overload the water system with toxic chemicals and metals beyond natural proportions. The Mediterranean, Baltic and Arabian seas and the coastal areas of Atlantic, Pacific and Indian Oceans are too polluted today with chemical and metallic wastes.[17]

Countries like Japan, China, Indonesia, India, the members of the EEC, Canada, USA, Russia and others, having long access to the seas and lakes, obtain marine fish in abundance. But modern man is not only receiving bounties from the waters, but also carelessly and sometimes criminally damaging the balance in water systems by polluting them with hazardous wastes, oil spills or toxic chemicals. Disturbing the natural balance is well marked in coastal areas with their hinterlands. About 60% of the world population, i.e. over 3 billions live within 100 km of the shoreline and 95% of the world fish catches come from in-shore areas. Marine pollution today is creating a catastrophe in this in-shore area particularly in industrially developed zones. In spite of some regional preventive steps, mostly taken in the 'postmortem' stage, the situation in general is very alarming. Contamination in the Mediterranean and Lake Baikal waters are classic examples of human malfeasance. Many rivers of the USA, China, Russia and India are similarly contaminated with industrial and agricultural wastes.

Two dominant pathways through which the pollutants reach the seas are: the rivers and the atmosphere. Metals like lead, copper, cadmium, iron, arsenic, nickel, zinc and chemicals like PCB, DDT, CFC and HCH make their way through these pathways in the forms of water-flow, rain, and acid rain. The dumping of wastes, including nuclear and industrial, have become even more hazardous in the last two decades. Excessive harvesting of whales and seals and, incidentally dolphins and polar bears which are entirely of no use to us, are other examples of exploitation and pollution of land and marine resources.

Oil spills are another sore environmental problem. Besides the recent spills of the nineties in the Arabian Gulf, Russia and the USA, there were multiple disasters caused by oil tankers, as illustrated in a chart of UNEP in Appendix 2.

In Kuwait the oil fires ignited by the retreating Iraqi forces in almost 700 oil wells spilled about eleven million barrels of crude oil into the Arabian Gulf and burned huge quantities, for months, with a total loss of over 1.5 billion barrels in 1991. Approximately 22,000 tonnes of sulphur dioxide (SO_2), 18,000 tons of soot and thousands of tonnes of carbon monoxide and nitrogen oxides were estimated to have been emitted every day from these oil wells. Think about the environmental pollution this oil spill caused to land and aquatic life throughout the Middle East and beyond.[18]

Alhamdulillah, this problem is under serious consideration by environmental activists. That is how some of the Conventions and Protocols from the world community to arrest the deterioration started taking shape. The Convention on Wetlands of International Importance, 1971, the Convention on the Prevention of Marine Pollution by Dumping of Wastes, 1972, the Prevention of Pollution from Ships, 1973, the Prevention of Marine Pollution from Land, 1974, the Convention on the Law of the Seas, 1982 and the International Whaling Convention are some of the laudable steps taken in this area to control the disaster. Unfortunately the implementations of these Conventions and their legal enforcement are dangerously slow, due to the ethical and spiritual blindness of the parties involved. Protocols and Conventions without regulatory bodies charged with their enforcement remain pious wishes only. We tend to forget the lessons of history that the historic mighty civilisations grew near the waters of the Nile, Sutlej, Indus and Ganges rivers, and of the growth of Rome, Carthage, Alexandria and Athens on the Mediterranean Sea.

Moreover, human beings are composed mostly of water. Our tissues, membranes, brains, hearts, sweat and tears all reflect the same recipe of life: H_2O, the molecular formula of water, is 71% of the human body. Other components, like carbon, nitrogen, calcium, phosphorus, etc., compose the earthy part of the 'clay' (*at-teen*) from which Allah ta'ala mentions that He created human beings. Science does not contradict, rather it confirms the concept of the Noble Qur'an and the fragments left of other revealed Books that all living beings are created out of water, and man is created from clay, a mix of 'earth' and 'water'.

> **"We made from water every living thing."**
> (Qur'an 21: 30)[19]

All the major religions, which have any connection to their original revelations, honour water, including Islam, Christianity, Buddhism and Hinduism. Yet it is shocking that their followers don't hesitate to pollute it beyond its natural created capacity to restore itself to balance. That is how, by our own actions, we bring damage and catastrophe upon ourselves. Water pollution causes disease, suffering and death to millions of people, both in developed and developing countries. Are we not committing wrong actions by our enormous pollution of water, the source of our life and living? Are not those of us who believe in the Creator and His creation of the world betraying the trust, with which we are charged, to use and not misuse His creation and creatures? To use is to maintain the balance in nature, the nature created with certain order and balance by the Creator. When Adam, peace be upon him, was created, he was entrusted with wisdom and knowledge, and it is said with knowledge of the elements of nature of which even the angels were not aware. Humans as successors to Adam and Ibrahim, 'alaihima's-salam, have acquired more of this knowledge through generations which, like their predecessors, they are entrusted with (*amanah*) to protect the creation and not to misuse it.

But modern man, sometimes negligently and sometimes with the Christian notion that Jesus washed away all his sins by crucifiction (I seek refuge with Allah from the concept), or the sense of 'dominon' of Genesis, pollutes the earth and its waters immeasurably.[20] Modern egocentric humans in the name of developmental GDP and GNP have been damaging and degrading the balance of nature with all of the five pollutants mentioned above.

The seven seas, our main reservoirs of water, have been rising and falling slightly to keep the natural balance, through different geological periods. But recent global warming, caused by different polluting actions of the industrial revolution, is exceeding all known limits. Global warming is raising the sea level by melting the ice caps of the North and South poles. The scientific prediction is that the present rapid state of warming will submerge the coastal areas of Bangladesh, India, Egypt, China, Indonesia, Mozambique, Thailand, Philippines and parts of the American and European coasts, including Norfolk, Lincolnshire and Holland. Rich countries like the Netherlands may try to avert the situation by raising more and bigger dykes, which may or may not prove effective, but the poorer countries will suffer disasters unless the pollution is arrested forthwith, and maybe even then it is already too late as some scientists have contended. (See *Saving our Planet*[21])

Even our daily drinking water supply is contaminated through multiple pathways: leakage of storage tanks, fertiliser and pesticide percolation, lead pipes and toxic wastes, industrial and municipal discharges, landfill and septic tank leakages, and through air pollution.

We all must take care of these pathways. Local water supply authorities should invariably test the drinking water, and consumers should verify their rights and be alert. The Safe Drinking Water Acts of different countries have not been always safe enough, as their administrators have not always been ethically oriented. Even renowned bottled water companies have been found at fault. For drinking, carefully home treated water can sometimes be found more safe.

Material pollutants are damaging the global environment but we must not forget that moral pollution is the root of this disaster. Unless we awaken mankind to its moral and ethical obligations to the earth and its multifarious things and beings, we cannot meet the challenge of the disaster.

The developed countries of the North have already taken some emergency steps to arrest this catastrophe in forms of Clean Water Acts but the developing countries are suffering its immediate pangs, causing death, disease and ill health. Malaria, cholera, typhoid, dysentery and diarrhoea are taking toll of million of lives in the developing countries due to dirty, polluted and unhygienic water supplies. Other types of disease and suffering caused by all the five major pollutants are increasingly coming to the attention of the WHO and other health watch institutes. Slow poisoning by some pollutants like nuclear fuels, PCB, DDT, CFCs are now commonly visible both in the industrial North and the developing South, in horrendous proportions. Chemical accidents like Bhopal and nuclear accidents such as Chernobyl are no longer few or far between, although the aforementioned are some of the most dramatic. Pollution has reached the state of being a genuine disaster not only in the water but also in the air, land and atmosphere, which we will analyse further. They are not only directly causing deaths, but leaving the atmosphere seriously polluted, causing long-term damage through greenhouse effects, acid-rain, holes in the ozone layer, warming of the earth's seas and atmosphere, and metallic pollution of the soil and water.

1.5. Air Pollution

Only a few years after World War II, I was in London as a student. New construction of roads, buildings and factories was going on at a high speed but the marks of the devastation of war were quite visible. Ravaged buildings, deep craters, damaged roads and factories were a common sight. People still talked of blackouts, sirens and aerial bombings, death and injury, food rationing and other sorrows and sufferings. What I found in the morning newspapers was no less harrowing. A *Times* headline drew attention to the number of deaths that occurred during the years of 1952-1953, due to heavy smog, which reached an alarming figure of 4,000 in London alone.

Even scientists, health authorities and environmentalists were shocked. Smog caused deaths in New York and Amsterdam in 1963 and 1966 and in later years. There is no definite figure of deaths available in similar conditions in cities like Tokyo, Bangkok, Birmingham, Paris, Berlin, Moscow and Warsaw, but even today you see the horrible smog in cities such as Bangkok and Warsaw causing not only deaths but associated diseases like bronchitis and asthma. This environmental catastrophe is caused by various pollutants let loose in the air and water, by industrial and agricultural metallic and chemical emissions in enormous uncontrolled quantities.

During the last few years another phenomenon was noticed both in Eastern and Western countries. In some European and American cities you find less cold and snows than before, with more floods and cyclones. Even in the desert city of Jeddah, where I was resident for more than twenty years, I saw more rain and greenery than had previously been common. In Jeddah, which is one of the most ancient cities wherein lies the grave of humanity's mother Hawwa (Eve) 'alaiha's-salam, one sees greenery all around. When one drives on modern desert highways to Makkah and Madinah – the two harams – one finds more grass, vegetation and fruit trees along the roads than before. In the flooding on the day in 1991 on which speed-boats were plying near my house on New Jeddah roads, the residents had to evacuate their plush villas with huge losses of their valuable carpets, furniture and gadgets.

Water and air, the life-line of man, animal, bird and plant, and the climate are in serious jeopardy today because of human actions. We sometimes put the blame on natural calamities – flood, cyclone, rain or snow – forgetting that such calamities are the after-effects of sustained violations of divine guidance in all fields. When we waste, pollute or misuse these divine bounties in nature we only think about our personal or chauvinistic national needs, ignoring the fact that only Allah is the Creator and owner of these life resources and man is only a custodian or trustee of their use on a universal basis. After all, mankind have a common origin in Adam, 'alaihi's-salam, although now split into different geographical and political entities. No one can live without water and air, which are vital elements of the universal system which we identify as nature. It is the duty of every man and woman to keep it clean and unpolluted. The average man takes about 500 million breaths in a lifetime. Everyday he uses several litres of water. Allah has allowed living beings a certain margin of impurities for purification through nature's system but we are exceeding that margin far beyond its natural capacity and are creating problems and disasters by polluting air and water.

Emissions into the air are from both natural and man-made sources. Natural sources include both animate and inanimate elements, i.e. plants, forests, fires, volcanic eruptions and emissions from land and water. UV rays and the infrared heat of the sun are also natural elements of the environment. But man-made pollution created by the five organic and metallic pollutants mentioned above are degrading the water and atmosphere everyday.[32]

According to one UNEP report 99 million tons of sulphur-oxides (SOx), 68 million tonnes of nitrogen oxides (NOx), 57 million tonnes of suspended particulate matters (SPM) and 77 million tonnes of carbon monoxide (CO) were released in one year only (1990) by human activities. Major contributions to pollution comes from OECD countries in spite of their monitoring initiatives since 1960.[10]

Some American and European countries have passed laws for protecting the environment from air and water pollution. But air and water cannot be localised, so global protective measures are necessary, more than ever before, to arrest the imbalance created by these gases from the industrial nations.

Nitrogen oxide is produced by burning fossil fuels like oil, coal, and gas, and by volatile organic compounds which slowly escape into the atmosphere. They include unburned hydrocarbons of automobile fuel, industrial chemicals and even plant and arboreal chemicals. In the atmosphere these chemicals combine due to the heat of sunlight and rays affecting ozone and other gases. Toxic gases are produced by: oil refineries and coal burning, military and civilian nuclear facilities, industrial and agricultural factories and their dumps, coal, oil, gas and nuclear power stations, dry-cleaning establishments, refrigeration and air-cooling equipment and vehicles such as cars, buses, trains, aeroplanes and power boats.

Besides common industrial and vehicular emissions, the nuclear accident of Chernobyl in 1986 and the chemical accident of Indian Bhopal in 1984 are some of the classic examples of such pollution. The recent discovery of a hole in the ozone layer in the southern polar regions, since followed by numerous other holes, is another appalling landmark in the degradation of the global environment. Production of CFC and halons has been on the increase since 1930, as refrigerants, aerosol propellants, foam and fire retardants. Sulphur dioxide is also produced by these fuels, further producing acid in the atmosphere. Carbon monoxide is another gas produced by burning these fuels polluting the atmosphere. The set order and discipline of these gases' productions cannot be changed by scientists or ecologists at the moment; that is in the hands of global industry which is demonstrably out of control. But what man can do is to ascertain these facts of creation and maintain that discipline by controlling their related activities with care and caution, and moving to bring industry and its global driver, finance and banking, under rational control. What man has been doing for ages is just to go for material development without caring about its consequence. The after effects of man's pollution, especially in the industrialised countries of the North, with its long lasting consequences, are no longer minimal. They are distinctly evident in the greenhouse effect, the ozone hole, smog, acid rains, respiratory problems, cancers and other diseases. These problems and diseases cannot be confined to regions of origin as the air and water travel freely without passports and visas.

The high pollution visible in the atmosphere is not only causing problems to man but also to the animals, birds, fish, vegetation and forests all over the world. This disaster has not even spared inanimate objects. The wear and tear on the Taj Mahal of Agra, the Acropolis of Athens and the Coliseum of Rome are standing examples of atmospheric degradation. According to UNEP studies the industrial countries of the North are the worst culprits. Alhamdulillah, the majority of the world population, i.e. 58%, live in the countryside, and in the South this percentage is much higher, but the situation is changing fast and the ghettoes, busties and shanty towns are crowding all the big cities of the East creating enormous health and hygiene problems.

Besides air pollution, the lack of a clean water supply, inadequate refuse disposal and very poor housing and medical facilities pose a great menace to city dwellers and rural populations. This enormous pollution problem went unnoticed by scientists and ecologists until very recently, denting science's misplaced and fallacious reputation for omniscience badly. Acid rain in Sweden and other places aroused the world's attention and stirred environmental activists to help organise the conference in Stockholm in 1972 under the auspices of the United Nations, a milestone in world awareness of the disaster. Since then, within the last twenty years, individuals, groups, governments and local and international institutions have been active in trying to save man from an environmental cataclysm of the worst order. The most recent event was the Earth Summit of Rio de Janeiro of June, 1992. The difference between the developed and developing countries is yet wide and varied but mankind cannot afford this difference, or any delay in prompt handling of this catastrophe. The UN and other national and international bodies ought to rise in unison to save mankind from this ignominious destruction of inanimates and animates on earth; why that is not happening or only happening so slowly that it is irrelevant to the urgency of the situation, we will examine in some detail later. The landmark declaration of the Earth Summit on environment and development is self explanatory and is widely and publicly available.

This declaration has reaffirmed, with greater emphasis, the Stockholm declaration of the Human Environment Conference of June 1972. The goal is to establish: a new and equitable global partnership through the creation of new levels of cooperation among states, key sectors of societies and the people, working towards international agreements with respect to the interests of all and to protect the integrity of the global environmental and developmental system, recognising the integral and interdependent nature of the earth, our home.

With due respect to the efforts and aspirations of heads of states and governments, it must be said that, in spite of the grave situation of pollution, no enforceable obligation of the concerned states or authorities was undertaken. The most important factor of control or management of the environment was not even considered in its two dozen and three principles enunciated in the Declaration. How can those principles succeed without moral commitment and legal adherence? Nothing is legally binding and nothing is ethically dictated therein. Implementation of the resolutions will be voluntary by the concerned parties of the North and South, come what may.

The bedrock of the difference between the developed and developing countries still remains in material interests only, without any moral or religious motivation. No doubt the earth is our home but they are ignoring the universe and its order and discipline, set by our Creator, which must be preserved by us, not as ruthless masters of 'dominion' but as moral and legal trustees of the Creator. The origin of creation is the supreme Lord, **"Badi'u's-samawati wa'l-ard" "the Originator of the heavens and the earth",**

(Qur'an 2: 117) Who is kind and merciful but we must be true to our covenants to Him.

Generally, scientists and economists lead us to believe, out of their own materialistic secular beliefs which they imagine confirmed by their experience, that nature is infinite and is at human disposal and that growth is progress wherein science and technology will solve all our problems. So man can manage the planet earth only on a material basis, as we are so advanced! They implore us to solve the environmental and developmental problems only by recycling waste, composting food products, controlling emissions and conserving forests. They ignore the vital need of moral awareness and responsibility and the regeneration of an ecologically sound society as opposed to egocentric norms. Their beliefs are confined to short-term material benefits as against the universal existence. They tend to forget the Infinite Universal Being Who set the universe of stars and planets to abide by certain rules and orders. We earthlings can disobey that order only at our peril. The environmental disaster of today is the consequence of our disobedience to that Supreme Order of our Lord and Creator. The uncertain chaos of an accidental Big Bang is not our premise, since it begs the question of Who set it in motion, and Whose are the laws which every single atoms has followed since that first posited explosion. The faultless order – as divinely ordained in nature in water, land, atmosphere and the universe at large, requiring man, if he is to be in harmony with that order, not to waste or plunder but to use and develop with a universal moral regard, with the intention of peace and harmony towards all creatures who are submitted to their Lord – should be the mainstay of our faith and action.

The premonitions and warnings of natural disasters – cyclones, earthquakes, floods, draughts, famines, diseases, wars and accidents – should remind us of our disregard for the divine order and the guidance sent through the divine Books and the Prophets. The countless creatures of the universe are not just material objects, they have spiritual and moral existence too. Humans are not the only living creatures in the universe; there are millions more lives and species, some known and some unknown, who all have their correlated interdependent rights and obligations. The sooner we realize this cardinal fact, the sooner we will begin to avert the disaster. The sombre divine guidance is:

"The sun and the moon follow courses computed; and the herbs and the trees—both prostate in adoration. And the heaven He has raised high, He has set up the balance in order that you may not transgress (due) balance. So establish weight with justice and fall not short in the BALANCE. It is He Who has spread out the earth for (His) creatures."
(Qur'an 55: 5-10).

"... Who created the seven heavens one above another; no want of proportions will you see in the creation of the Most Gracious. So turn you the vision again; do you see any flaw? Again turn your vision a second time, your vision will come back to you dull and discomfited, in a state worn out."
(Qur'an 67: 3-4)[19]

1.6. Land (Soil) Pollution

Pollution is not confined to water and air alone. It is now widespread on land also. Land contains not only the soil but everything standing on or lying underneath the soil, such as forests, insects, plants, buildings, animals, birds and other species. Humans also live on land and they are created from clay. Land also contains the minerals of coal, gas, oil, lava and other things. All reflect a beautiful orderly system of the green earth of plants, crops, vegetation, fruits and flowers. Only He, by His divine power (*qudrah*), originated and set them in order and humans neither created nor set their natural ordering. Land is only 25% of the earth's area, with water occupying 75%. Land is the principal habitation of humans, animals, birds, insects and many more forms of living species. They all survive on water, soil, air, plant life and other substances provided by the Creator in His measured way. That divine measure we must know and try to maintain for our own survival and benefit. The amounts of oxygen, hydrogen, carbon dioxide and other elements of life, are fixed by the Creator in due measure for all living things. Since all things and beings are mortal, the Creator in His set discipline provides or deprives one of them of some necessary elements for life or death. Man is gifted with the volition to keep himself healthy by maintaining that divine measure or to make himself sick by its degradation. We are growing crops, building cities and destroying civilisations, following or violating that supreme measure. Human population is increasing by leaps and bounds, but the land mass remains the same for thousands of years. So unless man uses the land according to that set order, human sufferings and want may be acute and irreparable.

Land is not just a barren field rather it is gifted with green fields and forests, hills and plains, waters and minerals, tropical, deciduous and coniferous forests, deserts and snow-covered regions, and enormous varieties of excellence and beauty. Each one has its own natural characteristics as willed by the Creator. Man in his volition disturbs these characteristics, sometimes unknowingly but sometimes knowingly, with short-sighted egocentric reasons. Excessive violation of the measures creates unnatural imbalances polluting the natural environment. Man, over a long period, in ignorance or obstinacy, has already exposed the land to heavy pollution, to the serious detriment of the global population and other beings. We have to know about the state of our actions and their natural consequences.

We use water for improving our industrial and agricultural prosperity; we also misuse water by wasting or poisoning it. Thus we pollute the land by using it or its produce too much or adding undesirable chemicals to it for short term personal or national gains, ignoring the totality of human benefit. This misuse is not only careless but criminal, causing environmental degradation.

Deforestation

Forests are some of the most valuable natural assets on earth. But we indiscriminately cut or burn forests for some material benefit, without realising the global consequences for rainfall, climate, desertification and soil erosion. We erect dams to divert water channels without taking proper cognisance of the ecological effect on upstream and downstream inhabitants. We deposit lethal chemicals and hazardous wastes on lands of developing nations, without considering their dangerous effects on the neighbourhood and beyond. We burn forest, coal, gas or oil and even spill the oil without even thinking that it is generating too much heat and killing living beings, and polluting the global atmosphere.

Forests are rightly considered the lungs of the earth as they extract huge quantities of carbon dioxide from the atmosphere and emit the oxygen essential for life. Wide deforestation in North and South is creating dangers for rain, soil and living species. Tropical forests cover 7% of the land mass but they contain about 50% of the world's plant and animal species. With the loss of forests we also lose rare plants and species. Forests are the source of some foods, medicinal herbs and industrial raw materials. The decreasing forests of Brazil, Indonesia, Argentina, Malaysia, India, Vietnam, Thailand, Africa and of the European continent might give us some resources to enrich ourselves temporarily but surely, in the long run, it is diminishing our most valuable natural resource, degrading the global environment beyond repair. These forests are major sources of human food and drink both in North and South.

Forests provide fuel, building materials, fodder, and industrial raw materials in all continents. About two billion people in the world still depend on wood as a fuel, for their domestic and manufacturing energy needs. Soil takes thousands of years to form but takes only a few years to destroy. It is estimated that 15% of forest lands stand degraded by human actions. This is caused by cutting, burning, water erosion, wind erosion (often caused by reckless removal of hedges and other natural shelter), chemical use and physical interference. Over-grazing, deforestation, and agricultural over-exploitation are some such degrading acts, sometimes done for necessity, real or imagined.[33]

A real threat to the global water system is the massive change in land use and patterns of deforestation which affect the hydrological cycle. The tropical rain forests mainly store water in plenty, so when forests are cleared for industrial needs, more and more they lose the catchments of water and soil. Forests also produce rain clouds so with their extensive loss by fire or logging, rains taper off, resulting in less moisture in the air. The severe climatic effect of this deforestation has been noticed with alarm in countries like Brazil, the Amazon basin towards Peru, Colombia and Bolivia. The same effect is prevalent in deforestation in Thailand, Indonesia, Malaysia, India, Ethiopia and other forests of Africa and Asia. East or West European forests are no exception to this degradation. Forest fires are more frequent in the USA and Australia, and thus cause more environmental damage than logging.

According to one estimate, Western Europe has lost 70% of its forests since Roman days. Even the US has lost 33% of its forests since the days of Columbus. Before 50 years ago, 25% of the Indian subcontinent was covered with forests, but today it has only about 10% left. At the present rate of deforestation, the rain forests of India and Bangladesh will be wiped out in the 21st century of the christian era. That is why some scientists and ecologists calculate environemental doom to be only 100 years away while some predict it be only 50 years at the present rate of degradation of the environment.[23-25]

Allah, exalted is He, says in the Qur'an:

> **"Mischief has appeared on land and sea because of (the meed) that the hands of men have earned."**
> (Qur'an 30: 4)

Ice-free areas of land mass amount to several thousand million hectares. Out of this, 31% is forest and woodland, 24% is pasturage and 11% is cultivated land. Out of 32,000 million hectares available for cultivation, only half of it is cultivated in spite of the huge population boom. It is clear that the Malthusian theory of population and the Darwinian theory of struggle for survival do not take account of the abundant supply of humans and of the natural resources of land, water and air, over millions of years of the earth's existence.

Some scientists, economists and Judaeo-Christian experts take it for granted that natural resources are infinite and man as their master could exploit and control them by science and technology. But today we find that by their lack of regard for ethical, humanitarian and divine norms a colossal environmental imbalance has been created all over the world. Recent awareness of the environmental pollution caused by the agricultural and industrial revolutions has horrified the same experts. They find a world disaster of unprecedented nature aproaching today in all areas of the ecology and environment. Some experts believe that doomsday is not more than one or two decades away. In any view, man must adopt quick sure measures of correction both in the moral and material fields.

The Qur'an warns man to ward off this mischief done by human hands and to seek refuge from all mischiefs. (Qur'an 30: 41 and 113: 2-5) It is a clear warning to man to desist from wrong action and corruption against the measured norms Allah ta'ala has set in nature for the benefit of man and other creatures. The Prophet Ibrahim, alaihi's salam, thousands of years before 'Isa, and the Prophet Muhammad some hundreds of years after 'Isa, peace be upon them all, laid down the same rule in Makkah and Madinah for conservation of the green earth. In a tradition of the Prophet Muhammad, salla'llahu 'alaihi wa sallam, narrated by Jabir ibn Abdullah, radiya'llahu 'anhu, he said:

> "Ibrahim declared Makkah a sacrosanct city. I do so for the Madinan territory between the two Harrabs (about a 12 mile belt). No tree of this city shall be felled and no animal shall be hunted down."
> Muslim[26]

This was a particular law for the two sacred cities, and so it is not universal, but it does accurately reflect the Prophet's teachings that impinge on the environment, for example the prohibition of needlessly destroying crops and trees.

What modern conservationists of forests and animals are doing today is actually extending the norms laid down by our prophets for the environment. Muslims still practise this norm for Makkah and Madinah, the citadels of Islamic civilisation, and take this norm as a guideline for their treatment of animals and forests in general. The last Prophet, salla'llahu 'alaihi wa sallam, even extended this norm to the whole earth in another authentic tradition:

"The earth is green and sweet and verily Allah has installed you as trustees in it in order to see how you act."
Muslim.[26]

He also said in another tradition that if a Muslim plants a tree or sows a field and men, beasts and birds eat from it, all of it is sadaqah on his part.

Abu Bakr, radiya'llahu 'anhu, the first caliph of Islam asked his army, which he sent to attack the Byzantine armies in Syria, to convey them the message of Islam and told Usamah bin Zaid, radiya'llahu 'anhu, the leader of the expedition:

"Do not njure the palm trees nor burn them with fire and do not cut fruit-bearing trees."

This remains an injunction binding on all Muslims during war and peace.

Thinly populated areas of Alaska, Canada and Siberia grow huge forests of wood but today face a real threat of greedy human exploitation. Thickly populated areas of South East Asia and Latin America are dwindling in their abundant green forests. Brazil, Bolivia and other forest-rich countries are now taking conservation efforts and it is hoped that it is not too late.

Deforestation for development is taking a heavy toll on the environment, hitherto unnoticed by scientists. Unless the trend is reversed the present disaster may destroy the whole global ecology. At the present rate of logging, all unprotected old growth forests of Washington and Oregon will vanish within 25 years according to the *Environmental Almanac* of 1992. The Almanac also says that Canada has lost 60% of its old growth forests due to heavy logging. South American countries are trying to follow them for their own economic growth and for repayment of their huge foreign debts or more realistically to service the interest-debt on loans that are clearly unpayable. Here we encounter the villain that we will increasingly come to realise drives the entire war being waged against the environment: global finance, the monetary system and banking.

Tropical forests not only maintain the vital balance of oxygen and carbon dioxide but also provide invaluable sources of wood, plants, fruits, spices, nuts and vegetables. Herbal medicines from the forests are becoming more and more important with the modern scientific affirmation that they do indeed contain life-saving drugs, but they are becoming scarce with deforestation. The tropical forests are located mostly in the developing countries whose natural resources have enriched the developed countries for ages, but now these countries are heavily indebted and cannot repay the loans imposed on them with such burdensome interest. The one trillion dollar loan of these countries cannot be repaid or even serviced without deforestation of their rich forests. Total deforestation in these countries may pay the pound of flesh but not without oceans of blood. The price of that blood is a disaster for the whole earth, including the developed countries.

These heavily indebted countries of the South are also paying their debts through cheap rice, coffee, cocoa, jute, timber and cheap labour, but they can never catch up with the inflated cost of industrial finished products monopolised by the North with their high interest charges of the 'free-market economy'. Christian countries legalised interest only in the 16th century though it is prohibited in the Bible. The Muslim countries adopted their practice, much later when they were colonised by the Western empires. The World Bank, IMF and other banking institutions are playing the role of greedy Shylock. The divine order is 'do not take or give interest'; but does anybody care? (Qur'an 2: 274-280)[19]

Our land is valuable not only for human habitation or agriculture or industry but also for water, timber, fish, birds, species, animals, minerals, and wildlife habitation with the natural genetic reservoir and cleansing agent, biodiversity. Even the wetlands, which we consider as lying waste, are the actual source of many biological agents enriching our ecosystem. They help regulate the water cycle by slowing and storing flood waters; they prevent the erosion of shorelines; they also help produce oxygen and atmospheric nitrogen which support the living systems of the plants and other species. Some wetlands even filter out heavy metals, caliform bacteria, pesticides and toxic chemicals. Nature seems so conducive and wonderful in its various features that man forgets that the order and discipline behind it is not by accident but by the supreme balanced creative act of the Creator. The creation is so vast, orderly and magnificent that erring mortals can do best by following that flawless discipline without luciferian rebellion.[27]

We must use these multifarious gifts set in nature without misusing them for the short-lived profit motive needed for a standard of living assumed to be every man's right. The very existence of man is so minute in the scale of the earth and the vast universe that we must not venture to upset its balance by thoughtless actions dedicated to idols such as GDP and GNP. In scientific subjects like ecology and environmental sciences, to talk or write about moral or spiritual values would have been considered irrelevant or reactionary, specially to Marxists and secularists, before the present environmental disaster became clearly apparent. Theologians or philosophers, like scientists, gave rare attention to environmental problems even thirty years ago, but the enormity of the problem has dragged all and sundry to care for the widespread environmental catastrophe. E.F. Schumacher, in his book *Small is Beautiful*, held in 1973 the importance of the relationship between technology and sociocultural issues.[28] The ethical connotations of environmental issues are now being studied by various universities and institutes in the West and East. It may restore the lost conscience of humanity and our dormant value judgment from the dungeons of secularism and communism. It certainly seems that the ruling Judaeo-Christian world élite are not capable of seeing beyond their own narrow vested interests. If the living deen of Islam can bring back its followers, and through them the rest of humanity, to the core of divine guidance free from conflict, a great service may be rendered to humanity in general and environmental issues in particular.

Al Gore, now the Vice President of USA, in his book *Earth in the Balance*, opined:

> "Whether we believe that our dominion derives from God or from our own ambition, there is little doubt that the way we currently relate to the environment is grossly inappropriate. But in order to change, we have to address some fundamental questions about our purpose of life, our capacity to direct the powerful inner forces that have created this crisis, and who we are. These questions go beyond any discussion of whether the human species is an appropriate technology; these questions are not for the mind or the body but the spirit."

He goes further to say:

> "Indeed it may now be necessary to foster a new 'environmentalism of the spirit'".[8]

His analysis and conclusion may not be agreed upon by all scientists and technocrats but it lays a deep emphasis that material concern is only one of many human concerns and cannot be duly approached without ethical and religious moorings. He contends that religions:

"mandate an ethical responsibility to protect and care for the well being of the natural world."
(pp 238-243)

In the main, two distinct types of forest encircle the globe. They are:

a. The tropical rainforests girdling the equator where rainfall is plentiful throughout the year. The trees there are mostly broad-leaved evergreen although there are a few conifers. There are about 200 varieties of these trees including teak, sal and mahogany;
b. Boreal forests of the North which are mostly coniferous like oak, maple, poplar, pine, firs and larches; a less common species than the broad-leaved ones. They are also mostly evergreen but oak, maple, and larches drop their leaves at the end of summer. Outside these two broad global varieties forests are more varied and mixed in size, colour and growth.

Like all living creatures the trees also need nutrients to survive, which they take from wet soils, air and from the sunshine, through leaves, roots or trunks. For their size and growth many nutrients are stored inside, away from the environment, as with man, animals, birds and other living species. Any inclement environmental conditions affect them like human beings; these signs came to the attention of scientists and ecologists only in recent times. But Allah gave this knowledge to all His prophets such Adam, Nuh, Musa, Dawud, Sulayman, 'Isa and Muhammad, 'alaihimu's-salam. They always advised their followers to maintain the environmental balance, as we see in their traditions.

Forests are rich in wild-life so we find thousands of species of animals, birds and other species there in abundance. With deforestation by cutting or burning we destroy these lives, their nutrients and biological diversity ruthlessly. Moreover, the potential for valuable herbal drugs extracted from forest vegetation, by physicians and chemists, old and new, is also greatly reduced by widespread deforestation.

Forests play a vital role in protecting soils and regulating water supplies throughout the globe. Deforestation leads to washing out, drying away or blowing away of the soil's fertility by rain, sunshine and air. If the soil is exposed to sun, rain or storm for a prolonged period you are left with unworkably hard tracts as in the Sahel countries, Indonesia, Brazil and India. Forest soils are known to absorb ten times more water than those stripped of forest cover.[29]

About 50 million tribal peoples who live in the forests in India, Brazil, Indonesia, Zaire, Madagascar, Australia and America, are the people worst affected by deforestation. Besides the massive economic and ecological problems faced by these poor people due to deforestation, they also suffer in the loss of their hearth and home, their own culture and identity and the source of their humble living. Go and see their miserable plight in Assam, the Amazon valley, the USA and other locations, before talking of technological development and industrial progress assessed in terms of GDP and higher standard of living. Faraway cities and industrial centres are no less affected by the climatic implications of deforestation in their loss of high quantities of carbon and oxygen and the production of carbon dioxide consequent on the burning of forests and fossil fuels.

Experts now warn that, with an area about the size of Germany being deforested every year, the world's rainforests may be obliterated within a few years. (See *Imperilled Planet*[30])

FAO, in one of its reports, throws the blame on the poor landless cultivators and wood-fuel collectors for causing 50% of tropical forest clearance without realising that what they do is no doubt intended for their survival but is at the instance of the rich. Some of these experts sitting in the ivory towers of the UN tend to forget that these poor people "are mere pawns in a general's game".

These industrial or commercial 'generals' are supported by the so called market economy of free enterprise, making the rich richer and the poor poorer and pawns. In the hands of the leaders of the market economy, the World Bank, the IMF, and other banks, based on bloodsucking interest-taking and giving, manipulate the global economy for their profit to the serious detriment of social welfare, genuine economy and environmental cleanliness. Even major countries like Brazil, India and China have to toe the line exposing their people to natural and man-made environmental disasters. The miseries of their deforestation, dam construction and floodletting are too common nowadays. Even Britain, Russia and the USA are not immune from the eco-disaster of today, as it engulfs the whole world. About 50,000 sq. km. of primary rainforest are degraded worldwide annually by the timber industry. Softwood is used by the industrial countries as throwaway goods after its use once (rarely twice) in packing, etc. Hardwoods are used mostly by those countries for furniture, fittings, railway sleepers, shipbuilding and other jobs, requiring woods from developing countries like Indonesia, Malaysia, India, Brazil and tropical Africa. Logging is the major culprit in this game of degrading the rainforests, causing soil erosion, loss of species, loss of biodiversity, emission of carbon dioxide, removal of valuable oxygen and loss of watershed protection. A few are getting richer at everyone else's expense and at the cost of the degradation of the global environment affecting billions.

Conservation of rainforests is an old and laudable initiative to save a major source of food, shelter and medicine for mankind, but today it is all the more necessary to balance the air that we breathe, to cleanse the water that we drink, to preserve soil for cultivation and preserve the multifarious species who interwoven form our life cycles. Sometimes economic pressure is cited as the justification for clearance of the tropical rainforest. However, in 1989, scientists working in Amazonian rainforests found that the yields from sustainable use, including selective harvesting of timber, fruits, nuts and other plant products and medicine were higher than those from non-sustainable use.[10]

The temperate forests are equally under siege from commercial and industrial deforestation. In Canada, the USA, Europe and Australia, the pattern of forest destruction is similar in logging for industrial, commercial, agricultural and urban development, resulting in serious environmental disaster. Erosion is so severe in some mountainous areas that it is resulting in desertification. The Ethiopian drought of 1984-6 was mainly caused by deforestation with resulting erosion of topsoil and loss of vegetation.[33]

According to one estimate about 225 million hectares of tropical forest will be cleared or degraded, out of 2,998 million hectares of world tropical forest, within a few years at the present rate of deforestation. According to a UNEP estimate, 75 million acres of closed forest and 3.8 million acres of open forest are disappearing every year. According to the World Bank, 12% of Brazilian and African forests had been cleared by 1988. Unless conservation efforts are carried successfully all closed forests may disappear from the earth, creating serious environmental imbalance.[10, 31]

According to another UNEP estimate, shifting and expanding agriculture accounts for 70% of deforestation in Africa, 50% in Asia and 35% in America with very little left in Europe. About one million species found in tropical forests may disappear without conservation efforts. Deforestation in the upland watersheds of India, Pakistan, Bangladesh and Nepal is causing sedimentation in the downstream rivers damaging their reservoirs and irrigation systems and costing about $1,000 million a year. The

UNEP, UNDP, UNESCO and FAO are jointly trying to take remedial measures but their red tape-ism and materialistic approach may not save the day.[10]

1.7 Noise Pollution

Noise is a frequent pollutant of the environment. Except for the noise of thunder, storm, earthquake or volcano, noise went unnoticed before the industrial revolution of the 17th century. The noise of wars was not uncommon but bomb blasts were fewer before Noble's detonation in the 17th century. But today the man-made noises of factories, trains, cars, bombs and aircraft are all too common and too widespread.

High pitched noise disrupts the senses of all beings. Vibration of a body imparts motion to the air which in turn is transmitted to the ear in a sound wave. The basic function of the ear, created in the embryo, is to reduce the sound waves into electrical or neurological signals to the brain nerves of a living creature. High pressure sound affects the eardrums, made of an elastic membrane, and the nerve cells. Brain nerve or hearing loss can result from prolonged exposure to intense sounds and blasts. Animals, birds and humans can all be touched by this loss, affecting ear and brain efficiency. This noise pollution may affect you while at work or at home, both physically and psychologically.

Various countries of the world have adopted legislation in recent days to prevent noise pollution by engines, cars, aircraft and industry. Anglo-French Concorde flights which make huge noise while breaking the sound barrier are banned in some countries or airports to meet the standards of noise pollution. Some high noises are banned at night and near hospitals, residential and educational areas, to avoid this pollution. We may not find this world to have quite the tranquility of a hermit's cage, but to live and let live in peace and quietness is your birthright.

POLLUTION

General

If someone asked you to believe that today's world is as polluted as Hiroshima and Nagasaki were in 1945 by human acts, you might laugh at him. Nevertheless, the fact remains that on a global basis the situation has become much worse than even the aftermath of the 1945 atomic pollution in Japan. We have seen above how the five major pollutants have degraded world ecology and the environment on land, and in the water and atmosphere, bringing all of us to the brink of collapse. We have also seen how the land, water and atmosphere are collapsing due to the so-called revolutions in the field of agriculture and industry devised by human ingenuity without regard for the ethical and spiritual values of the interdependency of all animate and inanimate forms in the cosmos.

Both the free and the socialist worlds have built on a common ground of material development envisioned only in terms of GDP and GNP, where ecology and morality hardly count. A hitherto undisclosed database now reveals a harrowing tale of catastrophe: not fable or fiction but hard reality. An unpredictable situation created by man, worse and wider than Hiroshima; this time not by war of man against man but by a relentless war of man against the creation and the Creator. To understand and appreciate this catastrophe we have to deal with some of the following effects, well known to environmentalists but not so much to the common scientist or the public. They are:

The Greenhouse effect
Acid rain
Holes in the Ozone Layer
Nuclear proliferation and
Desertification

2.1. The Green House Effect

The planet earth, like the other planets of our solar system, was created out of the nothingness of a nebulae, from the vast amounts of gaseous hydrogen and tiny traces of elements, by the sovereign Creator with well measured, cosmic law and order. The creation – this solar system and possibly millions more like it – is vast and expansive but well ordered in its nature. Those who don't recognise these basic data of the creation of the universe by an All-Knowing Creator, but travel in the wilderness of materialistic and hypotheses of an accidental big-bang and then the evolution of species, are considered by some the master culprits of the environmental catastrophe. The big-bang and evolution might have been processes caused by the Creator but they are definitely not shown to be the ultimate source of our existence by any logical or scientific process of deduction. The environmental catastrophe has brought us nearer to the understanding of that truth.

The upholders of these so-called 'scientific' hypotheses have never gone uncontested theoretically, but they seem to have smooth sailing with vocal but short-sighted activists. They cannot visualise the might and magnificence of the spirit lying behind all material existence. They have the proud products with them of the agro-industrial and technological revolutions of both capitalism and communism. But now it is admitted by the same scientists and technocrats that such material revolutions have reduced the earth to the present ecological nightmare.

Theologians, moralists or spiritualists could not evoke human interests or divine or humanitarian considerations as much as the present disaster called for. Only very recently the activists of Islam, Christianity and Buddhism have come forward to attempt to handle the situation, very slowly but firmly. The Noble Qur'an categorically guides man to uphold the balance established in nature with justice and to not fall short in it:

> **"The sun and the moon follow courses (exactly) computed; And the herbs and the trees both bow in adoration. And the firmament has He raised high, and He has set up the BALANCE, in order that you may not transgress (due) BALANCE. So establish weight with justice and fall not short in the BALANCE."**
> (Qur'an 55: 5-10)[19]

The Creator orders His creatures to maintain the balance with justice and equity, and man with intelligence and volition should not disturb, rather he is asked to maintain, that balance in nature and society. He is asked to thank and praise that Sovereign Lord of the worlds, not of the planet earth alone, Who is kind and gracious:

> **"Praise be to Allah, the Lord (the Cherisher and Sustainer) of the worlds (the universe), Most Gracious, Most Merciful, Master of the day of judgment. You (alone) do we worship and Your aid (alone) we seek."**
> (Qur'an 1: 5)[19]

The temperature balance in the earth from the Poles to the equator is maintained by radiation from the sun in our solar system. Solar radiation passes through the atmosphere to keep the world warm enough and good for its inhabitants – men, animals, plants and other species. Scientists have only discovered this balance which is a result of *Qudrah* (divine power and decree), but they can neither set nor control it nor can they create life or substance. The earth radiates a part of the heat back to space to keep that set balance. Gases such as ozone create a shield for the earth which prevents harmful ultraviolet penetrating in too great quantities to the earth. Carbon dioxide on the other hand traps some of the radiated heat, reflecting back a part of it and keeping the earth warm and at just the right temperature ordained by the Creator in His infinite wisdom and by His Qudrah. Without this dual protective shield of ozone and carbon gases the planet earth would either be scorched by ultraviolet or freeze below 20° Celsius and become lifeless like other cold planets around the sun, as we know today.

This latter warming up of the earth through protective carbon dioxide gases is known as the "greenhouse effect". In excess this effect leads to an overheating of the earth. The two main gases whose actions in excess are polluting are carbon dioxide (CO_2) and methane. Other greenhouse gases include nitrogen dioxide (NO_2), halons and CFC (chlorofluorocarbon). Massive burning of fossil fuels such as coal, gas, and oil by man for electrical power and industry, along with deforestation, have already increased the levels of CO_2 highly, warming up the earth more than its temperature is in its natural balance. It was hitherto unnoticed by scientists blinded by pride in their material progress.

Scientists and ecologists today measure that burning of fossil fuels alone is releasing the alarming quantity of 5 to 20 billion tons of colourless and odourless CO_2 every year.

This has increased the temperature of the earth, especially after the industrial revolution of the West. The pre-industrial level of CO_2 is estimated at 260 -270 ppm (parts per million) by volume which has risen to over 350 ppm by volume today and may rise further causing the deterioration of the entire global environment. It is estimated by experts that at this rate, CO_2 emissions from the burning of fossil fuels alone may reach to 600 ppm at the beginning of the 21st century. With huge emissions from fossil fuels and heat from nuclear power stations, even though there are almost nil emissions from solar and hydroelectric power consumption, the balance instead of going back to pre-industrial levels may deteriorate further. Further deterioration in the situation of the ozone layer has been confirmed today by the expansion in the hole over Antarctica, and the appearance of many more holes over many parts of the world.[32-34]

The remedy is said to lie not in increasing industrial growth but in containing the increase of CO_2 emissions with conservation and diversification of safe methods of obtaining power. An increase of 2-4% is predicted per annum, unless drastic remedial steps are adopted, taking global warming up by 0.5 degrees centigrade. (See Appendix 3 a chart of increasing temperature).

Besides industrialisation, urbanisation is also a major contributory factor to the greenhouse effect. So, some sociologists strongly suggest that we 'go back to the villages'. It may be a debatable issue, but it is an argument not without force or justification for both environmental and socio-economic reasons. Even modern agriculture with its machines and fertilisers is not immune from creating appreciable emissions of CO_2 and other gases. Pollution control cannot achieve reversal of the entire process but correction is essential in various fields, and perhaps it will not happen from a technological motive alone but with moral and social commitment.[5, 17, 21]

This warming up has already adversely affected the climate, wildlife, agriculture and human health, in a way hitherto unnoticed by man. Areas near the Poles have longer and warmer growing seasons, while higher temperatures in the areas near the equator and tropics are adversely affecting food production according to ecologists. As a result of the warming up, oceans are rising and polar glaciers and ice caps are melting, thus raising the sea level. This can also flood the low-lying islands and coastal areas around the globe on all continents. A little more imbalance invites unknown disaster to habitation, plants and crops in countries like Bangladesh, Indonesia, India, and the coasts of the American and European continents.[32]

It is estimated by ecologists that the English Channel and the North Sea could rise by several inches within the next fifty years, affecting their coastal populations. Without higher barriers, even London could be submerged under water or become a canal-navigable city like Amsterdam or Venice. The peril is being aggravated, not only by natural degradation of the climate, but by the global warming caused by the so-called industrial and agricultural revolutions. According to ecologists, CO_2 is responsible for more than 50% of global warming. (World carbon emissions are shown in Appendix 4).

In 1988 we went to Bangladesh from Saudi Arabia with a relief team of the World Muslim League and the International Islamic Relief organisation, and saw the unprecedented devastation of the flood. People saw the terrible destructive force of nature and most of them considered it an Act of God, in that modern sense that ascribes disasters and momentous events to God, as opposed to the tawhid of the Muslims who see the existence and movement of every atom as being from and by Allah. Was it just an 'Act of God' or rather the aftermath of accumulated human follies, wrong actions, disobedience and mischief?[5] If an 'Act', His Act must have been invited by human follies as a warning or punishment. Was it in Bangladesh alone? Mark the other catastrophes of 1988: severe drought in Midwestern USA; hurricanes in different countries; severe forest fires worldwide; flooding in India; a heat wave in Europe and America.

Think about the effect of all these disasters on ecology. The more we eulogise material progress, which comes at the price of ethical degradation, the more disasters we have descend upon us. Sometimes we talk of moral regeneration, but for material gain only! We cannot ignore material needs but it must not be at the cost of higher values. Some talk about the greenhouse effect as an Act of God but is it not invited by and a natural consequence of amoral and even immoral human acts?

2.2. Acid Rain

The burning of fossil fuels produces oxides of sulphur and nitrogen. In sunshine these compounds create photo-oxidation which, when it descends on plants or soil, its effect is strongly acidic, capable of damaging plants, forest, soil and water, and thus of course it affects all life forms.

The term 'acid rain' includes rain, sleet, snow and mists which have been acidified by these compounds. Acid rain was not confirmed by scientists until the late sixties. It has been clearly detected that when fossil fuel gases are released into the atmosphere, hydrogen peroxide acts as a catalyst and turns them into sulphuric and nitric acids. They easily travel hundreds of miles in the atmosphere before they fall to earth as acid rain, polluting and damaging. This rain also liberates heavy quantities of aluminium in the respiratory systems of men, animals, birds, fish and plants and other living species obstructing them from absorbing the required quantity of oxygen for their health and survival.

Acid rain in Norway, Sweden, Scotland, Canada and the USA awakened the sleeping conscience of the scientists and forced ecologists to meet, under UN auspices, and devise measures to contain it on national and international levels through laws and protocols. So far it has destroyed 70,000 sq. km of forests in European countries alone.[35-36]

According to one UN estimate, in the field of producing greenhouse gases, the USA's contribution is highest, followed by Russia, Brazil, China, India, Japan, Germany, the UK and Australia. It is causing a reduction in food production, increased health hazards to men and other beings, soil erosion and deforestation, water pollution, drought, flood and incurable diseases.[37] If not controlled by effective national and international measures there will be no-one left on the earth to fight for his or her survival. It may bring peace, but the peace of the grave with no need for food, drink or air. Mankind may be replaced by another species such as the cockroach, or the planet earth may quietly spin through space entirely depopulated of intelligent life.

Acid rain, urban smog, nuclear and chemical proliferation are all adding to global warming and other ecological disasters. Global CO_2 levels have increased by 25% and methane levels have doubled after the historic industrial revolution in Europe. The UN-sponsored IPCC estimates that the earth is destined to have a temperature a few degrees higher Fahrenheit in a few decades if warming continues at the current rate.[37]

Human predictions cannot overrule the divine measure and balance, but scientists rely on their mathematical data for future model forecasts. Data lead you to attempt to control your material development without ignoring the environmental catastrophe, if you are true to the facts. The industrially advanced countries of the North have a much greater responsibility to reduce these emissions of CO_2, to save the earth from a collapse which is looming large as a consequence of their own actions. The time at our disposal is not very much – some say only a decade or so. The authors of the book, *Limits of Growth*, estimate a limit of 100 years only, if corrective measures are not taken early[38]. In another treatise, *It's a Matter of Survival*, Anita Gordon and David Suzuki, estimate the time limit to be only a decade. They point out that materialistic contentions like "nature is infinite, growth is progress, science and technology will solve our problems, nature is at human disposal, we can dominate and manage the planet" can only lead us to the end of a tunnel, out of which there may or may not be an exit, but not to real safety or survival.[39]

According to *Vital Signs* of the World Watch Institute, since 1959 the CO_2 contents of the global atmosphere have risen by 13% largely as a result of the burning of fossil fuels.[40]

The Greenhouse Effect could be reduced by human efforts, mainly the conservation of energy.

Some recommendations are as follows: use of energy-efficient and, if possible, public rather than private transportation like electric rail, trams, and buses, and the use of carbon-free fuels in automobiles; use of energy-efficient lighting and insulation for public and private buildings and roads, e.g. fluorescent bulbs and advanced insulation; use of energy-efficient cooling, heating, washing and cooking equipment; support of renewable and alternative energy sources like hydro, solar and wind power; encouragement of energy free or energy efficient water and road vehicles. Acid rain is man-made and man has to control it both in the North and the South with determination and urgency.

2.3 The Hole in the Ozone Layer

Ozone is a gas in the atmosphere. It is an allotrope of oxygen with a molecular structure of three atoms (O_3) instead of two (O_2). Most of it is found in the ozone layer sixteen miles above the earth in the part of the atmosphere known as the biosphere. It acts like a natural filter that absorbs and blocks the sun's short wavelength UV (ultraviolet) rays which can be harmful for beings, causing skin cancers, and can be lethal for plant life.

A hole in the ozone layer, through which UV rays were leaking, was noticed over the Antarctic in the Spring of 1985. The depletion of the ozone layer was confirmed by some, but rejected by others as a scientific myth. This mock fight continued until NASA of the United States and the European Arctic Stratospheric Ozone Experiment confirmed the existence of a hole in the ozone layer in 1987 through their ozone experimental teams. This alarming fact brought the world to pay attention and prompted an international convention in 1987 to decide to phase out the production and use of CFCs by the year 2000 to save the earth. This was activated by the Environmental Montreal Protocol of 1990. Besides the burning of fossil fuels, which contribute to the Greenhouse Effect, another important danger of pollution has been detected in aerosols of spray cans like deodorant, hairs-pray, paint, etc., which destroy the ozone layer. CFCs and Halons are commonly used in: fire extinguishers, air conditioners, refrigerators, dry cleaning, electronics, furnishings and disposable fast food polyester packs.

CFCs in aerosols are some of the main culprits contributing to the opening of the hole in the Ozone Layer. Later, scientists discovered that the halon gases used in firefighting equipment, were even more destructive than CFCs in the opening of the hole in the Ozone layer so, by amending the Montreal Protocol of 1990, halons were also recently banned. But the time limit given for each under the Protocol still left room for more degradation of the environment. The amendments resolved on in London, Copenhagen and Bangkok up to 1994 have theoretically improved the situation but their practical implementation is terribly slow.

The US National Academy of Sciences recently reckoned that a 16.5% reduction in the ozone layer is possible if Freon gases continue to be released at the current rate, which will affect both human and plant life. The size of the said hole over the Antarctic is now reported to have grown to the size of the USA, while the ozone layer over the Northern Hemisphere is thinning continuously. CFCs and Halons originate from fluids in refrigeration and air-conditioning and also from plastics like styrofoam solvents used in the electronics industries. The Earth Summit of 1992 in Rio also considered the subject of global control of these pollutants, though not effectively enough. So came the amendments of Copenhagen and Bangkok as initiated and prompted by UN agencies. (Ozone depleting chemicals are shown in Appendix 5.)

Recent floods and hurricanes in India, Bangladesh, Japan and the USA, droughts in Africa and warmer winters in the northern hemisphere do not seem to be isolated incidents; rather the real aftermath of the pollution fallout on the earth. Today there are over one hundred national and international institutions, including the UNEP, busy researching and adopting measures to control this dangerous pollution of the global environment. We can only try, and hope that measures are not too late.

2.4. Nuclear Proliferation

The first atom bombs dropped on Nagasaki and Hiroshima in 1945 are alleged to have stopped the Second World War in its tracks, though this is contradicted by the fact that the Japanese were already negotiating their surrender. Whatever the alleged benefits, the damage caused to life and materials was unprecedented. The effects of the radioactive damage are visible even today on men and materials in Japan. Radioactive fallout travelled far beyond the sites of the devastation, polluting air, water, materials and soil. Scientists are today horrified at the thought of any atomic blasts, as their long term and remote effects can be even more horrendous than their very terrible immediate impact and destruction.

Fire damages, but it can also be used for human benefit. Atomic power was similarly developed for producing energy for beneficial peaceful uses, in contrast to destructive warlike uses. The reactors were devised to produce electricity from the fission of the isotope of uranium, U_{239} produced from enriched uranium U_{235}. This was considered in the beginning to be a non-pollutant, because it had no smoke or visible emissions of chemicals, etc. Atomic reactors for the production of power became the fashion in developed countries, to meet their own electricity needs and also for export earnings. Until very recently, their manufacturers, the USA, Britain, France, China and Soviet Russia, kept secret the serious hazards associated even with peaceful uses. Radioactivity's services were extended to the fields of agriculture, medicine and other civil and military developments.

Accidents, big or small, in military use were kept secret, but some of the blasts in civilian projects came to public knowledge, to the horror of the public. Some of these accidents were repeated in spite of sophisticated safety and security measures. Accidents took place in nuclear power plants, in Windscale (later renamed Sellafield) in Britain in 1957, 1976, 1981 and 1985, in Kyshtyn in the South Urals of Soviet Russia in 1957, in Detroit in 1968 and New York in 1972, Brown Ferry in 1975, in Three Mile Island, Harrisburg in 1978 and Gareok Ratromex of the USA in 1985. These are some of the accidents that came to light. The most recent, but not the least, took place in Chernobyl in the USSR in 1986 and Goiania in Brazil in 1987 causing great damage to areas near and far. These accidents took lives of men and animals, poisoned food and drink, damaged crops and plant life, and still remain a health hazard and will do so for a long time to come. (A chart of rising use of nuclear power generation is appended in Appendix 6).

Estimates show that the fallout of an explosion of 30 megatons can cause the deaths of 420,000 embryos or newborn babies and the birth of 230,000 babies with physical and mental disabilities. The whole process of nuclear power production needs the following steps: the mining, refinement and storage of uranium, the transportation of raw materials and equipment, the design, installation and testing of the reactor, the conversion, enrichment and reprocessing of U_{235} and U_{239}, the production and distribution of electrical power, and the disposal of waste. All these steps have now been established as containing great risk to both life and materials; not just in terms of explosions of bombs or reactors, but also through leaks and dumping. Since the process involves both men and machines, mistake or misconduct can't be ruled out and every mishap is dangerous for the environment in both the short and long term. Even decommissioning power plants and missiles and disposing of nuclear wastes, in Europe and America, are posing great threats to mankind, especially when their civil and military administrations think along purely material lines, and motivate their activities thus.

The enormous power contained in the fission of single atoms in processes such as spontaneous radioactive decay, a natural process, can cause mutations in any living thing with which it comes into contact. Multiplied enormously in nuclear explosions and depending on the substance it impacts upon, the fire and heat destroys and deforms both animates and inanimates within its vast range worse than volcanic eruptions. The radiation, which travels far and may be transmitted enormous distances in the upper atmosphere if the wrong conditions prevail, also damages the environment with multiple effects on the lives and health of its victims for generations to come. It is almost as if it foreshadows the doom of the earth when it will be laden with too many evils and vices. The Qur'an warns about the Last Day:

> **"When the earth is shaken with her convulsion, And the earth throws up her burdens. And man cries: 'What's the matter with her?' On that day will she declare her tidings; for that your Lord will have given her inspiration. On that day will men proceed in groups sorted out, to be shown their deeds. Then whoever has done an ant's weight of good shall see it. And anyone who has done an ant's weight of evil shall see it."**
> (Qur'an 99: 1-8)[19]

Besides the radiation caused by atomic blasts or leakage from nuclear power plants and other places, all living creatures are exposed to natural background radiation. Some of it, cosmic rays, emanates from outer space and some from ground substances such as uranium and thorium present in rocks, soil and sea water, or Radon gas. Radiation is measured in 'becquerels' and one becquerel is one radioactive disintegration per second. Human beings receive some 60,000 becquerels of radiation on average from natural sources which is in balance with their biological structure. Radiation damages the body by bombarding the cells in the biological system with high energy rays and particles generated when an atom disintegrates. Humans, animals and plants have a protective mechanism within their fitrah (the divinely created natural disposition) to combat the damage and repair it. But a small addition to the natural radioactive level may cause disease or genetic defect. (*Imperilled Planet*, pp 33-35[30], *Vital Signs*, pp 49 and 87[40]).

Nuclear power plants in the normal course of events produce an extremely dangerous cocktail of radioactive substances. Nuclear power processes increase the original natural radioactivity in the uranium millions of times or more. The high level wastes that result are so radioactive that they must be isolated from contamination for thousands sometimes tens and hundreds of thousands of years, to make their radioactivity harmless for living cells. Accidents apart from the low level wastes discharged into the environment within the 'safe' limit are also reported to be poisoning the environment speedily. However even the so-called low-levels which are reportedly safe are scientifically dubious and a matter still of controversy. (See *Imperilled Planet*. pp 35-36[30]).

In his book, *Eco Wars*, David Day estimated that there are 380 nuclear power stations operating in 26 countries with the highest numbers in the USA and USSR.[41] But a later estimate takes that number to 500, mostly located in the Western industrialised countries and hand-picked countries like Israel, India and and the now defunct Czechoslovakia. They all received the know-how, equipment and raw materials from the West. Countries like Britain, France, Germany, Sweden, Canada, China and Japan have most of the other stations. Pakistan, Iran, Korea and South Africa are also reported to be in possession of nuclear weapons and reactors. The colossal danger from nuclear power reactors are manifold and much more than from the military establishments of the West. In any view of the matter the world is sitting on a heavily loaded gunpowder keg ready to explode at any time unless proper material and ethical control is imposed. Unless the so-called superpowers come to their moral senses, just signing treaties can never bind them or others to obey mandates. Just look at the world nuclear arsenal possessed by the nuclear powers and think about its devastating destructive and polluting power. (See Appendix 7).

That is why a clarion call to the naturally religious masses and their spiritual leaders is essential to rouse their conscience . They must act through dialogue and solidarity instead of the brutal confrontation of 'crusade', 'dominion' or 'genocide'. These latter are the processes of the now defunct Judaeo-Christian world order. It is now time for the Muslims to stand up for revelation and its values. The world is aware of the diabolic destructive power of atomic devices so, when they apprehended an unthinkable military conflict between the two superpowers, they started a dialogue. Eventually they came up with treaties of non-proliferation. The most significant was the Nuclear Non-proliferation Treaty of 1963 banning nuclear weapons tests in the atmosphere, in outer space and under water.

Scientists discovered biologically dangerous amounts of Strontium 90 in cow's milk derived from nuclear tests in the upper atmosphere. This horrendous discovery provoked a worldwide outcry and led to the Treaty. Later the Nuclear Non-proliferation Treaty greatly helped to slow down the spread of nuclear weapons outside the inner club of the G5. This Treaty was due to expire in 1995 so the big powers were out to extend it for an unlimited period. Most of the developing countries have raised objections mainly on two grounds. Firstly, it should include atomic powers like Israel, India, South Africa, North Korea and the rest. Secondly the carte blanche monopoly of the five superpowers should also be restrained.

People feel that the United Nations has to take a new moral and ethical role rather than materialistic superpower diplomacy in this critically dangerous subject. However, the United Nations is the materialistic nations' attempt at forging a supra-national global government while retaining the hegemony of Judaeo-Christian control. Muslims know that the only ethical possibility in this age or in any age is the shari'ah of Islam. It can only be implemented by the restoration of the shari'ah in its totality an integral part of which is the Khilafah, which guarantees justice for people of every creed, and which intrinsically has an ethical use of resources and treatment of the environment.

When nuclear tests by the privileged class of the USSR, USA, France, China and Britain in land, underground, water and air go on unabated with special protection for their chosen countries the whole purpose of the Treaty, renewed through the United Nations in 1996, will be frustrated, and the United Nations seen for what it is, a club controlled by the people too heavily invested in nuclear power and weaponry to voluntarily forgo them.

A Treaty of 1972 updated in 1975 and 1978 took measures to prevent production and stockpiling of biological and toxic weapons. Another Treaty created a nuclear free zone in the South Pacific in 1986 and, after the collapse of communism in Soviet Russia in 1988, more treaties were in progress to effectively control nuclear proliferation and to engineer the destruction of nuclear stockpiles on a global basis. But, in spite of these, the nuclear club is expanding both for offensive and defensive purposes.

Because of aggression against Muslim countries being the fashion in the secular and socialist countries even after the demise of the cold war, the Muslims feel compelled to join the club. The aggression against Palestine, Afghanistan, Kashmir, Bosnia-Herzegovina, Chechnya, Azerbaijan, Pakistan, Mindanao, Rohingya and others creates a definite urge in their minds to defend themselves at any cost. They feel that it is not only a defence of their territory but also a defence of their common faith. Since friendly countries only render lip service and would rather try through their monopolised media to project the right of defence of faith as 'fundamentalism or terrorism', Muslims feel they must be strong enough to defend themselves. There may be some force in this argument but no-one has a right to pollute Allah's environment with something so utterly destructive as nuclear weapons or so permanently polluting as nuclear power, so we all must try for another remedy for peace. After all, Islam is the way to peace in name and purpose and it has to be demonstrated as such in all aspects of our life including the environment. You may or may not be a Muslim but the urge for peace should be your common desire. Peace serves not only mankind but it brings tranquillity in nature and environment. So, in the above analysis the Muslims have allowed themselves to be divided into national entities threatened on all sides by non-Muslim national entities further banded into supra-national forces to which they reluctantly allow the Muslims access. By this the Muslims have lost their original supra-national identity and their greatest power, which was exemplified by the Khilafah, whereby every Muslim who paid allegiance to the Khalifah was a citizen of one global Ummah of Islam with genuine political and military power, without the need for atomic weapons.

Lydia Dotto, in the book *Planet Earth in Jeopardy,* describes the direct and indirect impact of nuclear war:

> "In short it is possible that in the aftermath of a major nuclear war the global environment and human social and economic systems could collapse to an extent that might preclude recovery to pre-war conditions."[17]

The climatic effects and the likely consequences for ecosystems, the agro-industrial complex, productivity and ecology have been analysed to estimate its horrendous outcome. But its severe impact has not been duly considered.

One estimate (other than SIPRI – Appendix 7) showed that in 1983-1985 world atomic arsenals were over 50,000 weapons with a combined explosive yield of some 12,000 megatons, mostly owned by the G5. (USA, UK, Russia, China and France). To be precise, a one megaton (1 million tons) TNT bomb is five times more powerful than the bombs dropped on Hiroshima or Nagasaki in 1945. So a 12,000 megatons inventory is enough to destroy the whole human civilisation on planet earth, for what the blast didn't destroy quickly, radioactivity would destroy slowly and inexorably. This statistic does not allow for further increase by the G5 and others, nor for the 'star wars' programme of Ronald Reagan, and subsequent developments.

John Cairns in his book, *Rehabilitating Damaged Ecosystems,* assessed the outcome of nuclear war to be an unpredictable 'nuclear winter', where no life may survive.[42]

Out of 2,000 known nuclear tests about 500 were in the atmosphere and the rest were underground or underwater. Now it is realised that they did irreparable damage to the global environment. Today these tests don't go undetected due to high technological developments in satellite systems, but the damage done to the earth, its inhabitants and its civil and military personnel are still a guarded secret to avoid the wrath of the people. But the wrath of the environment is no longer a secret and for Muslims the wrath of Providence is not unknown. Are we not experiencing more volcanic eruptions, tsunamis (tidal waves), floods, droughts, famines and diseases than ever before? The publication *Earthscan* boldly pronounces that natural disasters are increasingly being seen to be man-made phenomena – the insurers' 'Acts of God' may soon be seen to be Acts of Man.[5]

After disasters, people and governments rush in with massive relief but that effort is also dominated more by political and economic factors than humanitarian and ethical considerations. In another title, *Our Drowning World*, Anthony Miller deals with the micro and macro-climatic syndromes of crowded cities and urban areas of the modern industrial world. Scientists, mostly though not unanimously, predict that the greenhouse effect will raise the climatic temperature by about 5 degrees Fahrenheit within the next century. This, in the history of the earth calculated today as 4.5 billion years, is very short. And this warming up is caused, according to the study, not naturally but by human actions.[43] Some scientists, who disagree, also assert that this is caused not by human actions but by changes naturally taking place in the core of the sun itself. More remotely, these changes may also be caused by the interaction of other stars and planets in the Universe, our solar system not being isolated from the rest. The revealed Books agree that the earth will meet a doomsday. Perhaps that doomsday will be caused by human actions, so that humans can receive the reward and punishment of their own deeds here in this life before the judgement of the next life and its more extraordinary rewards and more terrible punishments. Allah, ta'ala, says about that Hour before the Last Day:

> **"When the sky bursts open, ...When the earth is flattened out"**
> (Qur'an 83: 1-3)

The suffering of millions of people from inherited infirmities have been highlighted by Linus Pauling, in *No More War*[44]. Similar cases have been recorded by E.J. Sternglass in *Infant Mortality and Nuclear Power Generation*. Harrisburg, (1970)[45] and *Effects of Low level Environmental Radiation on Infants and Children*, University of Illinois.[46] Because of vested interests' desires for the profit involved in this new technological advance, the market was kept ill informed of its environmental effects, and indeed the market cared little anyway. Even today many facts of its colossal reactions within the body and the mind are kept top secret. They only press that the Nuclear Nonproliferation Treaty with all its loopholes be accepted by all except the old members (the Nuclear Club of the G5) of the Security Council of UNO. With this disparity again how can you restore the balance when there are about 200 sovereign countries of the world?

In Islam cleanliness is a part of faith which applies to clean water, food, clothes and environment. And in the environment there are not two standards for the rich and poor or the mighty and the meek. The Prophet Muhammad, salla'llahu 'alaihi wa sallam, was an embodiment of cleanliness in body, mind and in his environment, and a model of justice in every sphere of life. The sense of justice, equity and the rule of law practised in his life applied to big or small equally and equitably. As a model, Muslims look towards him in every problem they face and try to find the solution in the Noble Qur'an and in his customary practice, his Sunnah.

2.5. Desertification

Deserts are conspicuous in all parts of the globe. The Sahara and Kalahari deserts of Africa, and the Arabian and Gobi deserts of Asia are most well known but there are big deserts in America and Australia as well. Scientists and explorers were busy with their study for a long time and only in recent years it came to their knowledge that deserts are not static, but rather they are expanding fast into neighbouring areas due to climatic variations and human activities. Primarily desertification is due to lack of rain, loss of ground water level, or drought for continuous periods. This is happening more in recent years because of environmental pollution.[47-48]

Deserts are the world's driest places with little or no rain or water. Man, animal, plant, bird and other living species really only subsist there due to a small supply of water and other basic facilities. P. Meigs of UNESCO classified deserts into arid, semi-arid and hyper-arid areas based on annual rainfalls of less than 8 inches, 24 inches and one inch respectively.[49] In spite of their inhospitable environments the deserts are the dear homes of over 13% of the world's population most of whom are poor.

Surprisingly many of the world's famous rivers run through these desert areas: the Murray-Darling in Australia, the Rio Grande in America, the Indus, Amu, Tigris and Euphrates in Asia and the Nile in Africa. The old civilisations of Africa and Asia grew up there and survived for long. Islam was born in the desert of Arabia, grew up and always flourished in the deserts of North Africa and further afield, as well as in the fertile and agricultural lands of Persia, Iraq and the rest of the planet. Christianity and Judaism and their prophets were born and grew up in the fertile crescent and in the productive lands of Palestine.

The desert is a sandy place of fabulous contrasts of ruggedness and delicacy, life and lifelessness, windy storms and tranquil silence and it is a source of enormous power of matter and spirit. Its hidden resources of oil, gas and minerals are not small but its open natural scourges can be deadly. We all derive enormous benefit from its natural material resources, but its spiritual bounties delivered to us through scores of the prophets, many of whom were from the desert, remain ignored by modern man.

It may be asked, is desertification an environmental issue? That is how it came into the limelight in recent years. Desertification of arid and greenlands became so menacing in the Sahel countries of Africa that environmentalists had to come forward to combat it urgently. The attention of governments, private institutions and the United Nations came to focus on the disasters in the Great Plains of USA in recent years.

A desertification study group was first established in 1972 by the International Geographical Congress. Thereafter the first UN conference on desertification was organised in 1977 in Nairobi with a global agenda. According to Spooner (1989) this problem can be traced back to the medieval period or to an even earlier ancient period. But its menacing effect came to world attention in the second half of the 20th century. Dr. Mustafa Tolba, the former executive director of UNEP, pioneered its research and study. In *Sands of Change* (1987) it is pointed out that about 70% of the world's productive land is directly or indirectly affected by desertification involving about 900 million people in 100 countries.[50]

There has been some confusion and even conflict as to the exact definition of desertification but the fact remains that about one third of the dry lands area (the size of North and South America combined) are directly affected thereby; according to UNEP over three billion hectares are so affected.

The definition was begun in 1949 with French forester Auberville, and it is expanding everyday with more research data available. For a common understanding we may follow the official UNEP definition as: Land degradation in arid, semi-arid and dry sub-humid areas resulting from various factors including climatic variations and human activities. (Agenda 21 Chapter 12, Annual report 93). Hyper-arid areas of the Sahara, Arabia and Atacuma are to be included in this.

The global desert areas can conveniently be classified as follows:

1. The Sahara desert of North Africa covering over 3 million square miles, the largest on earth, from the coast of the Atlantic to the Mediterranean and Red Seas;
2. The Kalahari-Namib deserts in South Africa and in Namibia on and near the Atlantic coast;
3. The Sahelian deserts of Chalbi – Somalia, Kenya and other contiguous areas;
4. The Arabian deserts spreading from Sinai of Egypt, Palestine, Negev, Jordan, Syria, Iraq, to Saudi Arabia and Yemen.
5. The Indo-Iranian desert from Iran, Pakistan, Afghanistan to Indian Thar-Rajsthan.
6. The Central Asian deserts covering Gobi and Takla Makan in Turkestan, Mongolia and China.
7. Australian deserts covering about half of its land.
8. North American deserts including Nevada in Utah, Oregon, Colorado, Southern California, Arizona, New

Mexico and Texas.

9. South American deserts in Bolivia, Argentina, Peru, Chile and Equador.

The mapping of the deserts was done by Meigs for UNESCO in 1953, dividing them into thirteen areas. We have divided them into nine for easier understanding. This land degradation is not confined to the developing countries of Asia and Africa, but its impact on Central Asia (the Gobi in China and Mongolia), North and South America and Australia is quite extensive. The 'dust bowl' catastrophe of the great Plains of the USA in 1930, 1950 and 1970 awakened the conscience of scientists, politicians, economists and ecologists alike to combat it in subsequent years. Its impact on the Sahel, the Sahara, the Arabian and Gobi deserts are equally menacing, calling for united global action. UN efforts through UNCOD, the World Bank, FAO, UNESCO and other agencies are yet confined to study, research and monitoring, more than prevention and reversal actions.

The human causes of degradation are generally identified as over-grazing, over-cultivation with underground water, deforestation, salinisation, nuclear and chemical explosions, biomass burning and industrial pollution.

The natural ecosystem still remains the primary cause of degradation but the above human activities are contributing more and more due to our lack of awareness and care. Conceptual and other desertification monitoring by the UN and other agencies are becoming more significant than before but what is needed most are remedial measures both at local and international levels. The Rio Conference of 1992 estimated that about $300,000 million will be needed to tackle the problem over twenty years. Developed countries may finance their own projects but they are reluctant to share the costs of the developing countries.

Desert areas are increasing every year, both due to human activities and natural desertification within the ecosystem, affecting surface albedo, vegetation cover, agricultural production, loss of plant life, loss of ground-level water, the hydrological cycle, surface roughness with dislocation and loss of humans, animals and species. Its hidden resources like oil, gas and minerals can be fabulous but its scourge can be too deadly for those who defy the divine by recklessly failing to attend to its advance. The appended chart in appendix 8 shows global land areas of desertification.

Various measures to combat this gigantic global problem have been under discussion among scientists and ecologists. We may mention here some of them such as France Prequette of UNESCO who estimates the annual global loss of income as $42 billion in his book *Drylands and Deserts* (1995), Carl Zimmer in *Discover How to Make a Desert* (1995), F. Mayor in *A Halt To Advancing Deserts* dealt mainly with the Saharan menace in twenty neighbouring countries, H. Bregne in *Shifting Sands* (1993), Anne Shepherd in *African Report* (1992) and Catalina and Craig in *Earth Review* (1995) discussed primarily the Californian Desert Protection Act.[85-87]

UNEP and WMO initiated an updated report on desertification after the Rio Conference of 1992, which was published in 1996 as prepared by Martin Williams of Australia and Robert Balling of USA, under the title *Interaction of Desertification and Climate*.[85] After widely assessing the state of science on the subject they came up with ten fine recommendations for monitoring the status of desertification. But what about practical steps to combat the degradation? Maybe UNEP will come forward with some action programme backed by finance before the critical areas really turn into a global 'dust bowl', like the Sahelian deserts of Africa and the Great Plains of USA did in recent years, but what if they don't?

The UNEP started collecting facts and data for the entire globe from 1977 and eventually came forward with some practical proposals to combat it. Whereas the reclamation of desert lands is a necessity to accommodate development in industry and agriculture, desertification is taking a greater toll in all desert areas. So the UNEP came forward with the Plan of Action to Combat Desertification in 1991-1992 specifically for the Sudani-Sahelian region which included twenty-two contiguous countries of Africa. This plan might initially take care of desertification in other continents also, based on the data collected for the last twenty years.

Louis Berkofsky in his book *Progress in Desert Research* (1986) and other authors have suggested some measures for controlling desertification. They may not apply equally to all the deserts on the different continents, but they may be worth pointing out for those who want to seriously combat it. One such measure is planting and irrigation of strips of vegetation in terms of linear dynamics. A.S. Goudie in his book *Techniques of Desert Reclamation* (1990) has suggested means to control blowing sand and mobile sand-dunes, wind erosion and dust storms, soil conservation, water irrigation and plant and animal conservation.[89, 88]

In essence we have to take up each of the seven human causes of desertification as shown above and handle them all comprehensively and concertedly on a global basis and according to both scientific and ethical norms; not one without the other. It is only Islam, with its intrinsically global nature and its acceptance of other religions under the umbrella of shari'ah governance, that can solve these issues. Only then can we expect the climatic degradation in desertification to diminish.

WHO ARE THE POLLUTERS?

Pollution of land, water and air no longer appears a theoretical analysis but a practical manifestation visible in all sectors.

How deep and grave that threat is and how total a disaster we have to measure briefly in order to chart a course of global action. We also have to find the culprits.

3.1. Industry and Energy

Industry and energy are like the twin engines of an aircraft. One can't effectively operate without the help of the other. Nascent and small industries in the early days of civilisation were not that widespread. But the situation took a gigantic leap forward with the Industrial Revolution of the 17th-18th century in Europe. Electricity, the radio, powered ships, automobiles, trains, aircraft and factories outstripped agricultural production in a gigantic way. Factories increased, labour concentrated around them, transport and communications became faster and generation of power became a necessary corollary to industrial progress. Even trade, for raw materials and finished products, became the vehicle of industrial expansion, at home and abroad. Minerals like coal and oil, along with wood and hay, all became the mighty fuels of power production degrading the clean environment with emission of gases and other toxic residues. Electrical power became the essential tool of industry and also of domestic comfort. Pleasure and comfort became the standard of progress in the industrial West, ignoring or denying true spiritual and ethical values. Moral values and human brotherhood were sacrificed on the altar of technical civilisation. The dominant secularism initially, and dictatorial communism later, bade a ceremonial farewell to all the religions. The intellectual concept of secularism, that religion is a private affair, led to liberal democracy first and then to Godless communism. Both capitalism and communism, the by-products of the industrial revolution, vied with each other for material progress in the name of the industrial or the proletarian revolutions.

Industry took over the major fields of production and distribution, energy being its main tool. The industrial revolution in multifarious fields was based in Europe, but rapidly extended to America, Australia, Asia and Africa, with them acting initially as markets of consumption but later as manufacturers also. Today both the developed and developing countries of the world are bursting with industrial production using enormous energy from fossil fuels like coal, oil and gas, and nuclear power. The energy produced no doubt has brought the blessings of material progress but their uncontrolled use has severely damaged the environment by all-round pollution, perhaps beyond repair.

Pollution has already damaged the land, water and atmosphere enormously, going undetected by scientists and industrialists until very recently. This pollution is affecting not only the humans and animals but plant life, birds, fishes and all species of living beings. This is primarily by the human acts of production and by consumption of energy. In 1985, oil and gas together accounted for nearly 66% of all the energy consumed in the USA. Coal provided 23.7% and nuclear energy provided 5.6%. The USA relies heavily on these non-renewable resources more and more, and other developed countries are also following the same pattern.

Combustion of coal results in emissions to the atmosphere of sulphur, carbon and nitrogen oxides. Millions of automobiles release tonnes of carbon monoxide gas every day. And similar pollutants rise into the atmosphere from industrial oil, gas and atomic power, degrading the whole global environment. The increased use of automobiles which consume oil producing poisonous gases is shown in a chart. (See Appendix 9).

While the US is the largest overall consumer of energy the other industrial countries in Europe and Asia do not lag far behind. In 1984, the USA produced 22.4% of world energy and the USSR produced 20.4% of the total world energy output of 310.5 quads; France, Canada, the UK, Germany, Sweden and China followed them closely. Besides fossil fuel energy, nuclear power is the fastest growing source of energy even in developing countries like Taiwan, Brazil, India, Iran and Pakistan. The number of nuclear reactors in the world may have exceeded 500 by 1996, so the risks of more leakage and contamination are greater everyday.

Ours is not the first civilisation to have devastated its environment. The archaeological record is littered with the ruins of past civilisations which exceeded their ecological limits leaving behind them a degraded landscape. Today it is difficult to believe that the sands which now drift across the once splendid city of Babylon in Iraq used to grow the grain that fed a great civilisation, or that the barren hills of modern Lebanon and Palestine supported the vast Cedar forests which furnished the king and Prophet Sulayman, 'alaihi's-salam, with the massive amounts of wood to build the great Temple in Jerusalem. But they did, and it was human hands which later brought them to their present state. Stripped of protective tree cover, relentlessly over-grazed and exploited, these previously fertile lands fell easy prey to soil erosion and were quickly reduced to arid unproductive scrub or desert. A remarkable narrative of human acts of degradation, as pointed out by the authors of *Imperilled Planet.*[30]

The damage in one part of the world no longer remains confined there, rather it contaminates the entire global ecosystem through the free flow of water and air. The emission of gases, the toxic wastes and discharge of particles contaminate human bodies, forests, mangroves, wet-lands, waters, fish, animals and other species. Even material things are not spared by this horrendous pollution. The contamination of Love Canal near Niagara falls, Baikal Lake and Chernobyl of Russia, Bhopal of India and the nuclear leakages of the UK and USA are only a few examples of accidents. But daily pollution by industry and energy is limitless. (An illustration of global carbon emissions is attached with Appendix 4.)

According to some scientists in some billion years our sun will die and with it, all its planets, including the earth, may disappear or become lifeless. That is perhaps a little remote. But the longevity of non-renewable resources is estimated to be very short at the current rate of consumption: there may be coal for 200 years, oil for less than 100 years and gas for less than 150 years. This is all based on human assumptions as our scientific knowledge is limited, but their exact reserves and how long they will last is known to the Lord only. If we obey His discipline and commands, He might increase the life of these energy sources or bless us with new resources. He only guides us within our limited life to keep the balance set by Him. By satanic zeal we humans are disregarding that code of balance in the field of industry, in the name of development and progress. Human profiteering is our zeal and goal instead of sharing the profits of renewable and non-renewable resources with other things and beings. The zeal of consumerism and profit-making by the industrial countries and their industrial collaborators is inspiring others to follow their path of devastation rather than conservation.

Having consumed 80% of their known oil reserves the US is now importing nearly 50% of its oil needs. Worse is the situation of the other oil-importing countries of the North and South, who are out to consume more energy for more industrial and domestic needs, polluting the global environment more and more, resulting in a massive ecological and environmental disaster.

Among the alternative sources, nuclear power generation tops the list, with France meeting about 70% of its needs and the American and other European countries trying to catch her up. Its processing, operation, distribution, use, storage, transportation and waste disposal all add to the risk of radioactive contamination of the environment everyday.

So the need to develop more non-polluting hydroelectric, solar and wind power should now receive the topmost priority. We have seen that industry and energy remain the No. 1 culprit in polluting the global environment. So we have to conserve energy and diversify to use less polluting sources. Industrialisation must curtail its long swathe of destruction and deep appetite for exploitation and profiteering. The polluting industries and other offenders should also be made to compensate for the all-round degradation they have caused and are likely to cause. There should be an ethical and legal code for this to be set up and binding on everyone of the North and South. In the absence of a world government the UN has been looked to to take up this task earnestly and urgently, but has patently failed to do so, and makes no convincing moves in the direction of doing so. As we have said before, they have no global mandate from their Creator and Sustainer and so, even if we were to assume that their intentions are true and that the UN is not just a club of the super elite guarding its privileges, nothing they do, by the nature of things, will ever have any good result. It can only be by a global governance sanctioned by Allah, and that is the Khilafah, the rulership of Successors of the Prophet, sal-la'llahu 'alaihi wa sallam, that this disaster can be reversed if that is still possible. Remember, that the Khilafah of Islam which lasted almost 1,400 years until its recent interruption has no record of inflation, pollution, unemployment and destruction of the environment at all; all of these matters have only come about with the subversion of the Islamic Ummah, the overturning of the Ottoman Khilafah, the colonisation of Asian and African Muslims and the rise to global 'dominion' of the Jews and the Christians, many of whom once enjoyed the protection of the shari'ah within the lands of Islam.

3.2 Modern Agriculture

Even agriculture took the aid of industrial energy and became a tool of the industrial revolution for the increased food supply of the East and the West. The revolution talked of people but it enriched a few families and a few countries at the cost of others. It brought an image of prosperity which gave luxury and comfort to a few but enslaved others. The main casualty became the people of non-industrialised countries, known as the 'consumers' of the developing countries. It is now clear that it is the global environment which is the worst hit. Enough evidence is now available to indicate that pollution changes in climate have had an enormous effect on agriculture and livestock.

Technical, chemical and genetic methods applied to agriculture have become both a boon and a curse because of its unprotective methodology. As a result natural terrestrial ecosystems are facing serious degradation because of global increases in the atmospheric concentrations of greenhouse gases. It is estimated that even the climatic zones could shift several hundred kilometres towards the poles over the next 50 to 100 years. Flora and fauna may not shift that quickly, but a new disaster may reappear in the arid regions with water and moisture scarcity. Food shortage may reappear too, seemingly strengthening the Malthusian theory of optimum population and the socialist theory of unequal distribution. The green earth is becoming burnt, the clean water polluted and the fresh air degraded. Due to the heavy chemicals and fertilisers used, mass-produced agricultural products are no longer safe for consumption. Even the pretty flowers and green vegetables are not free of this contamination. Today the world manufactures many times more goods and chemicals than before the 18th century. Generally, industries contribute more to GDP and GNP in the North whereas a tug of war is going on in the South for its share between agriculture and industry. Due to developing technology, the rising burden of debts and the politico-economic subservience of the Southern countries, material development is less well advanced there, but it seems that they are better off in terms of the environment. However, they are not fully secure from its global impact.

Industrial development is so fast and seemingly fabulous that the startling achievements of yesterday appear outdated today. Robotics, automation, micro-electronics, computers, information technology, bio-technology and the space travel of today have dwarfed the conventional industrial revolution of yesterday. Similarly the energy that was dependent on coal, wind, gas, oil and wood are being overshadowed by hydroelectric, nuclear and solar energies. We tend to forget that sustainable development is not the result of human "dominion or exploitation" of the earth's resources, rather a gift of the Supreme Sovereign for human use, not for abuse or destruction. We all have a natural share in the bounties of Allah's creation, with a concomitant obligation of not harming others. Development or progress liable to injure others is not sustainable development at all. We have to respect and protect the divine order of the inter-relationship of things and beings, for any global development, far above "dominion" or "domination" of any region or race. Conservation of the ecosystem and human values cannot be treated as the sole obligation or monopoly of the West or the East. The agro-industrial imperialism and techno-political dominion of G7 may serve its members' interests, but it does not rule over the world's people and the global environment in a benign manner and on behalf of its peoples.

While we talk of negative and positive points of energy for industrial production, we forget similar points in the plants – carbon dioxide and oxygen, hydrogen and oxygen in living beings and the presence of other gases in measured quantities in all things and beings. We also ignore the fact of the creation of every living being in pairs – male and female. It is the positive and negative points of plant life that we experience in their exhalation of carbon dioxide at night and their photosynthesis of carbon dioxide into carbohydrates and release of valuable oxygen in the daytime. All living beings exhale carbon dioxide and breathe in oxygen, and plants breathe in and convert that exhaled carbon dioxide releasing valuable oxygen. Our exhalations are the inhalations of plants and their exhalations are our inhalations. The system in nature is so well balanced that one supplements the other during the day and night. Both points demonstrate the balance and order of the creation and that it is not a matter of "accident" or "evolution". Christian man's claiming god-hood and biblical 'dominion' over nature dislodged that order and balance. Unjust exploitation and domination of a few called for the destruction of all. We have to call a halt to this through the moral power of people. For that a strong awareness of the ethical dictates of the prophets is a must.

There must be no force or compulsion on people to enter a religion and certainly not to enter Islam. Islam, however, is the final revelation of Allah to the last Messenger, Muhammad, salla'llahu 'alaihi wa sallam, confirming all that the other prophets received, so much of which has been forgotten or twisted into the shapes that the other religions have given them today. Knowing this, Allah and His Messenger insisted that the Muslims must govern, extending justice to the people of all the revealed teachings and without compelling them to enter Islam. This has been the practice of the Khulafa of the Muslim community for 1,400 years. It is only the subversion of that Khilafah, and the dominance of Zionism and secularism and their usury finance that has brought the earth to the brink of catastrophe. It is only the Muslims, through the restoration of the Khilafah (whose inward is representation and trusteeship of Allah) who will save the earth and its people.

Industrial production and energy gave visible material growth no doubt, but its pollution severely degraded the environment, perhaps beyond repair. Modern agriculture became a guilty accomplice, through its mechanical and chemical tools. Modern science committed another gigantic mistake in not knowing its own impact on the environment before it did, and for even hiding it once it did know. Science ought to control through its technology but with ethical guidance and legal norms, however, these have long ago been cast adrift.

In Japan, the Minimata disease took a heavy toll for several years until scientists found out that the fishing village of Minimata was contaminated by the chemical wastes of quicksilver discharged into nearby water. Fish and mussels, the common food of local inhabitants, were poisoned by the industrial waste and were suffering from neurological, optical and other disorders due to the pollution. Pollution by industrial and automobile exhaust gas is very common in the industrial countries. Industry is using all the raw materials from the soil and water. Its multifarious products are distributed either through state monopolies or free market supply and demand. But the process of production and distribution is creating serious environmental pollution by all the five pollutants, i.e. natural, chemicals, fossil fuels, nuclear and minerals. 'Organic' farming may be an answer but without wider steps to contain the environmental degradation we will still be endangering our existence.

It is important for the environment to maintain 'biological diversity', though modern bio-technology is taking over its function both in animal and vegetable genetics. Paul Ehrlick defines biological diversity as: tens of millions of distinct species – and the billions of distinct population – of plants, animals and microorganisms that share earth with us. (*Habitat in Crisis*, 1987)[51]. Its maintenance involves the conservation of multitudinous life forms – from obscure plants and insects to well known species of birds, animals, mammals and fish.

The survival of wild species is concomitant with the ecosystem, including genetic diversity – one is tied to the other in the interconnection of life forms. It is a divine gift implanted in nature and we humans should never waste or squander it in pride, for any mere pleasure or dominion. It may not be legally binding on you but it is your moral mandate to conserve natural biodiversity – after all, we all must return to our Lord and render account of what we have done.[52] To preserve every cog and wheel of the life cycle should be the pivot of intelligent tinkering. Instead of destruction by deforestation or chemical abuse in agriculture, Muslims must awaken to conserve bio-diversity, and call others to Islam which is now the only conceivable refuge of sane people. The Assisi Declaration of 1986 for the first time adopted an inter-faith policy in the WWF Conference in Italy. This was followed up in The Ohito Declaration of 1995 in Japan:

We call upon the world's religious leaders and world institutions to establish and maintain a networking system that will encourage sustainable agriculture and environmental life systems.53-54

However, these attempts to tack together what they see as 'different religions' have never succeeded in the entire history of humanity, and there is no reason why the Christians and others should achieve it now. Allah's revelation is clear:

"The deen with Allah is Islam"
(Qur'an 3: 19)

"And whoever seeks other than Islam as a deen it will not be accepted from him, and he, in the next-life, will be one of the losers."
(Qur'an 3: 85)

In other words there can be no inter-faith concord by Muslims with other religions. Allah's truth is one, and all of His Prophets taught the same truth, but their followers over the generations distorted their teachings or forgot them, and Islam is the final revelation confirming everything that the ancient and recent Prophets taught. Our dialogue with the Christians, et al, is to invite them to Islam.

3.3 Toxic Chemicals and Gases

Out of 103 known chemical elements present in our planet, twenty are beneficially made use of by humans, animals and plant life; the rest are injurious to living organism, viz. lead, chromium and mercury. These three are used in batteries and cigarette manufacturing. Most of these elements and thousands of their compounds used in various industries end up polluting the environment. (*Imperilled Planet.*[8]) The US alone generates about 300 tonnes of hazardous wastes a year, i.e. more than a tonne per capita; more than half of it is solid wastes. Many synthetic organic chemicals are known to suppress or alter the biochemical processes of nature, and can cause diseases like cancer, birth defects or genetic damage to living beings. The incidence of bronchitis, pneumonia and asthma is now high among the Chinese, Polish and in other countries' industrial cities, due to the pollution of air by these chemicals.

Chemically produced gases pour in great quantities into the upper atmosphere from factories, power stations and vehicles across the globe, and fall back to earth as charged moisture in the form of smoke, cloud, rain, smog or snow. Our economic activities produce about 200 million tonnes of sulphur dioxide (SO_2) per annum, by burning fossil fuels. Europe alone produces more than 30%, North America produces a little less, Russia, China, Japan and the rest of the world produce the balance. These gases affect the crops, forests, vegetation and fish. They also affect human and animal organs, bones and blood, reducing immune systems of the body to disease and genetic degradation, as reported in these affected countries.

The US-owned Union Carbide accident of Bhopal in 1984 not only killed over 2,500 people directly but damaged the health of thousands, maybe millions more. The same was true in Chernobyl of USSR in 1986 from its nuclear reactor leakage. Another chemical – lead – present in petrol, used by the increasing number of motor vehicles, is a source of brain damage. In 1950, the world's motor vehicles burnt I. 4 billion barrels of gasoline; by 1980 the figure climbed to 5.5 billions and by the year 2000 may reach 10 billions. In spite of the legally obliged reduction in the contents of poisonous lead in gasoline in some countries, the amount of polluting emissions to the atmosphere is huge. (Appendix 9 shows the rising car production worldwide and Appendix 4 shows CO_2 emissions).

According to a London Times report of September 1, 1996, street pollution in London is worse than in Bombay, another city which is as dirty as Bangkok and Seoul. The research was coordinated by Harvard University, showing that London contains the highest levels of nitrogen dioxide produced from cars, power stations, gas appliances and cigarette smoking.

Toxic wastes that pollute the environment include pesticides commonly used in agriculture and horticulture in the West and the East. Most Western countries have phased out, are limiting or banning their use, but their export to Eastern countries goes on unabated. One WHO estimate puts the figure of pesticide poisoning at 400,000 people a year in developing countries, with 10,000 deaths. The excuse for the export is that it gives some improvement in food production; again the same market forces of profiteering prevail, the casualty being poor and needy human beings. Even animals, fish and other species and plants are also on the hit list of the free market forces of profit-making through production, distribution and consumption of these chemicals.

Industry is the most energy consuming sector of development, accounting for 37% of the total commercial energy consumption in 1990. In developing countries this percentage is much lower than 37% but in industrialised ones it is much higher than 60%. Some Eastern European countries and China also exceed the average of 60%, such as the OECD countries. According to UN statistics OECD countries with 22% of the earth's population consumed 82% of global energy in 1990. So pollution through industrial use of energy was the highest there, calling for drastic cuts and control. But these countries with political, economic and media control in their hands escaped the axe even in the latest Earth Summit of 1992, perhaps because the Summit had no genuine axe to wield.

The quantity and extent of industrial pollution depend primarily on:

a) types of raw material and fuel used;
b) technological and environmental controls in use and;
c) size and maintenance status of industry and its wastes.
So strict control of all these sources is necessary.

There being no global standard control, the situation is at the mercy of producers, who exercise mainly a voluntary restraint to avoid a backlash. Strict legal or ethical control is yet to occupy the field actively in the West or East, while time is running out. A multitude of industrial plants emit sulphur and nitrogen dioxides into the air, carbon dioxide, monoxide hydrocarbons and hundreds of trace contaminants some of which are lethally toxic. OECD countries maintain records of these emissions but not strictly and the developing countries are also trying to maintain records but not consistently. So the success of voluntary responsibility cannot be ascertained, but meanwhile global pollution is filling to the brim. Some countries of the East and West are taking remedial measures today, but public awareness and government responsibilities for pollution control are not forceful enough. One UNEP chart in *Saving Our Planet* indicates the extent of the catastrophe, vide bibliography and Appendix 9.

Emissions of pollution are not confined to the air, rather they are widespread on land, sea, river, and lake as well. Some garbage and industrial waste-water, produced in billions of cubic metres per year, are discharged into rivers, lakes and seas without any, or with merely minimal, chemical treatment. To understand the extent of the damage this waste water alone is creating for aquatic life and human beings one does not have to be a scientist or ecologist. Besides the increasing number of deaths, diseases – in the forms of cancers, respiratory problems, skin damage and nervous debilities – are on the increase.

3.4. Solid and Hazardous Wastes

Industry also generates millions of tonnes of hazardous solid wastes, mainly in OECD countries. These wastes are neither properly treated nor recycled, but dumped into known and unknown places with immediate or belated damage to life and environment. For example, staff of Dounreay, the nuclear plant in the North of Scotland, were in the habit of throwing nuclear waste, lithium and sodium and other matter down a hole in the ground which was in no way prepared to withstand leakage of seawaters, until one day the hole in the ground exploded and threw a highly dangerous cocktail of radioactive and other chemicals all over the landscape, from which they have allegedly been connected to a whole range of local child leukaemia cases. What was astonishing in this case was that top scientists did something that even secondary school children with minimal scientific education might have guessed could go astray; it is one of the most memorable chemistry experiments for most children when certain chemicals such as lithium are added to water.

Some efforts to stop repetition of hazardous disposal and accidents are already at hand, but the colossal losses of the nuclear accident of Chernobyl in Russia, the chemical accidents of Bhopal in India and San Juanico in Mexico are too notorious to be ignored. We have to take lessons from them. Some of these industries are operated by giant Euro-American corporations working for profit only.

An ounce of prevention is better than a ton of cure. Global attention needs to be focused on prevention in time, though in the present state of things the need for cure cannot be minimised. Recent protests against dumping of nuclear and other toxic wastes, in Australia, North America, Germany, Japan and other countries of East and West, should awaken the ethical and legal conscience of the authorities.

The rule of prevention and safety has to be applied to both conventional and state of the art civilian and defence industries. It may now be recognised that pollution by the defence industries is more important than their civilian production. There they produce the most destructive chemicals and nuclear weapons for their own use and for export earnings.

The use of chemical weapons has been common since World War I. Their trade in dangerous weapons amounts to trillions of dollars, a trade which could easily solve the essential food and environmental problems of the world. They spend too much on defence and keep global strife at a maximum to sustain their own GDP and GNP, at the cost of the developing countries. A chart of world military expenditure is annexed, for your evaluation of the cost and its impact on the environment. (See Appendix 10).

The Basle Convention of 1989 tried to regulate for the first time the trans-boundary movements of hazardous wastes and their disposal. Some countries like Britain, France and the USA are building huge industries for recycling, incineration or treatment of dangerous wastes, including nuclear wastes. Britain alone has a trade figure of £3 billion sterling for import and treatment of these wastes. Waste – treated and untreated – has amounted to so much that unless effective control is made obligatory the environment is at serious risk worldwide.

Some developing African countries are receiving these wastes for dumping, again on the profit motive, to enable them to repay their huge international debts. These debts are very cleverly engineered by banks of the industrial countries directly or through the World Bank, IMF or other banks, based on long term interest in the name of development. These indebted countries borrow more, beyond their capacity for political reasons, and end up as defaulters on economic grounds. The creditors are no less responsible for the whole debacle as they created the false credit in collaboration with the debtors. Old Shylock's drama is being re-enacted globally even today.

Fossil fuels, such as coal, oil and gas are finite and non-renewable in nature, but the whole focus is on them and remarkably enough they mostly belong to the developing countries, and, in the case of oil, almost exclusively to Muslims. These countries think that they need more energy to develop their essential industries, that they need more foreign exchange to develop their economic infrastructure and that they must take on huge debt repayments through their export earnings and finally, and a poor last, that they have to control the environment at heavy costs. They cannot stand on a par with the developed countries to meet their national obligations, yet the developed countries stress an equal sharing of the burden of pollution control. They ask themselves, "While the environment is mainly polluted by the industries of the developed countries, should the lashes be shared equally by the perpetrator of the wrong and its victims?" This issue is being debated while the world is burning, and countries like Malaysia embark on a fresh round of stripping the tropical rainforests for their highly profitable hardwoods, at the expense of their irreplacable conversion of carbon dioxide into much needed oxygen, and a thousand other losses.

At 1990 levels, the proven oil reserves were estimated at 140 billion tonnes of which 77% belonged to 12 OPEC countries. Coal reserves were estimated at 534 billion tonnes and those of natural gas at 104 billion tonnes. According to the estimates, the oil reserves will last for less than 100 years, coal for 200 years and gas for less than 150 years at the 1990 rate of consumption. The estimates may change for better with new discoveries, but environmental pollution is bound to be worse if not duly controlled by all concerned in the East and the West.

62% of global electricity was produced from thermal resources, 20% from hydroelectric power, 17% from nuclear power and 1% from other resources. So where is the remedy without conservation of natural resources and control of pollutants?

Today there are about 500 nuclear power plants, mostly located in industrially developed countries. Their pollution is also concentrated there but not confined there, as all pollution travels without passport or visa faster than human transport. The developing countries were losers, in the industrial race for raw material and manufactured products in the past, and are losing also at present. With 78% of the world population located within their borders they produce only 18% of manufactured goods and have only 14% of the world's commercial energy. Lack of technical know-how and capital investment and Western market protectionism also adversely affect their material development. They suffer equally under global pollution though they are less responsible for the catastrophe. To add insult to injury, wastes are mostly dumped in needy African and Asian countries or on Native American's reservations, irrespective of the hazards involved. Recent disclosure of Western hazardous dumps in Nigeria and Kenya alarmed ecologists, but with no immediate remedy in sight.

The US alone produces about 450,000 tonnes of commercial and residential solid wastes daily, and it is estimated that another 100,000 tonnes may be added by the beginning of the 21st century. A small portion of this solid waste is recycled but the rest is land-fill or dumped in water. Similarly, production and disposal in the industrialised countries is carried on with little care for the environment. PCB, a stable compound, is commonly used as an insulating fluid in manufacturing electrical transformers and capacitors, plastics, hydraulic fluids lubricants and inks. Its contamination can easily cause skin rashes, vomiting, abdominal pain, temporary blindness, genetic defects and miscarriages. Before the toxicity of PCB was well understood by experts, it used to be dumped in sewers and on the land, and still is. This is affecting all living beings, so it needs to be strictly controlled. A society of 5% of the world's population with a throwaway culture, generating about 50% of the waste, should not escape without penalty. Wastes pollute the environment in the land, water and air, so those who don't care about its consequences should be brought to book. Allah, the exalted, in the Noble Qur'an clearly says:

> **"Those who squander and waste are the brothers of the shaytan."**
> (Qur'an 17: 27)

Solid wastes dumped or put in trash for disposal include paper, cardboard, food materials, garden waste, diapers, sanitary towels, plastic materials, bottles, cans, tyres, metals, appliances, mattresses, packing materials and furniture from home, office and industry. Before throwing away for dumping or incineration these should be: a. reduced, b. reused and c. recycled according to the nature and risk potential of these wastes.

The emphasis should be on reduction of waste and reuse, wherever possible. Recycling is becoming more popular, with rising moral and social awareness of the environmental degradation. Recycling is cheaper and better than incineration or land-fill in the long term. It is possible and desirable for all cities and industrial areas, not for gain or profit but for our peaceful existence, to adopt these measures of reduction, reuse and recycling. In the long run it is gainful for the consumers and also for the global environment.

3.5. Travel and Tourism

Modern expanding travel and tourism is also posing a great threat to the environment, due to more use and misuse of air, land and water transport, currently with little pollution control. More than 80% of transport vehicles are produced and owned by OECD countries and they consume various types of fuel causing noxious emissions in land, air and water. Transport consumes 30% of the world's energy, most of it on land, producing 60% of the carbon monoxide, 42% of nitrogen oxide, 40% of hydrocarbon and 18% of carbon-dioxide emissions from fossil fuels. Besides this emission of polluting gases, the noise and vibration emanating from air, land and water vehicles are also of grave concern for the environment.

It is suggested that besides reducing oil and coal energy consumption, more use of natural gas, ethane, hydro-electricity, wind, and solar power may help minimise the high pollution. The use of fuel-free vehicles such as cycles, rickshaws, carts and boats is widespread in populous countries like China, India, Thailand and Bangladesh, with low costs and no burden being placed on the environment.

Some OECD countries and North America have already put some thought into fuel-efficient and lead-free vehicles, but the high increase in vehicle use is offsetting the possible gains. Some countries are experimenting with solar, electric and liquid gas transports, but the number of cars, trains and mechanical water transport vehicles is also increasing in both the North and the South, adding to the pollution. Air transport is also increasing faster than ever before, for national and global travel and for tourism. Land and water vehicles still carry the maximum number of people and volume of cargo worldwide. A greater control is needed in transport sectors both in the North and the South for arresting their toxic emissions.

Sun and sand tourists, while relaxing in comfort, forget that they contaminate the river banks and sea beaches with enormous amounts of chemical and natural waste. The North still attracts the maximum number of tourists with maximum pollution, but some historic and scenic Eastern spots and wild life reserves are becoming more popular everyday. While adding to foreign exchange earnings during the season they place an enormous burden on the environment, be it in London, Paris, Rome, Athens or

Istanbul in Europe, New York, Los Angeles, Florida, Rio or Montreal in the Americas, or Cairo, Carthage, Bombay, Bangkok, Manila or Tokyo in Afro-Asia.[55]

Nobody takes proper account of the moral and environmental pollution the tourist industry creates in these hotspots. We forget that man is not just a rational animal of physical satisfaction but a moral being of spiritual excellence too. Moral values tend to take a vacation in open clubhouses or casinos of drinking, dancing, gambling and womanising, with drugs, crime and violence. Sex tourism is a major attraction in the big metropolises of both West and East where minors, girls and boys, are traded. Tourists also pollute the environment in beaches, forests, gardens and transports, and clean enjoyment is hardly paid attention. The social, health, moral and environmental degradation that we are making in the process of travel and tourism will we hope not be ignored any more by people and authorities. The moral impact of the religions could play a great role in this field if they were in fact living faiths, however the religions other than Islam are largely decadent and distorted remains of the long forgotten teachings of the Prophets of previous versions of Islam. The very fact of their total ineffectuality is sure proof of the cessation of any living transmission within them. In the case of Islam, it yet remains for the Muslims to re-assert the preeminence of the revelation of the last of the Prophets, salla'llahu 'alaihi wa sallam, and to re-establish the shari'ah. Then it will be as it always was throughout our history that Islam is an embodiment of the ayah of the Glorious Qur'an describing the Prophet, salla'llahu 'alaihi wa sallam:

> **"And We did not send you but as a mercy for all the worlds"**
> (Qur'an 21: 107)

In our circumstances, it is clear that Islam always has been and will be again a mercy for all creatures, and for the environment.

3.6. War and Violence

Peace was first broken by Abel (Qabil) when he killed his brother Cain (Habil), according to the narrations of the revealed Books. He was the first human to murder another. He later repented, but the wrong was already done. In the same way, peace is broken between tribes, families and nations even in our so-called civilised world. Indeed, historians accept that the 20th century, which has the reputation of being the most advanced technically and in terms of scientific discoveries of every sort, is yet the most brutal and murderous age that humans have ever seen. Yet, it is an age that believes that it is progressing from out of savagery to a noble future. Invasion, conquest, rape, pillage and fighting continue and are on the increase in spite of all the so-called progress man has made for his tribe, family and nation. Material, carnal and physical desires goad man to strive for more and more egocentric pleasure, power and progress at the cost of others. Moral and ethical norms set by the Creator through revelation to the prophets, for the good of the creation, have been humbled to the whispering temptations of shaytan for dominion, power and petty material gain; sometimes even moral and religious arguments are advanced as justification. The more you hear about peace, the more warring situations deteriorate in the nooks and corners of the developed and developing regions of the world. Can any war be justified except for defence or fighting for the cause of your Lord?

In war and violence the victor and the vanquished both lose physically and morally. But the horrendous massacre, carnage, pillage and destruction continue, to the horror of human conscience, in all parts of the globe. All authorities try to justify their offensive actions ignoring the fact that they are accountable to their Lord. No one has ever escaped death, nor will anyone escape His judgment.

Primitive wars were localised but modern ones are not, especially as to their far-reaching consequences in terms of economic, political and environmental damage. Here we examine the environmental impact of local and global wars. The prolonged wars of conquest by Rome, Athens and Carthage, later ones by Mongolian Khans, Napoleon, Hitler and the Japanese Tojo, and current ones in different parts of the globe, all created and create widespread havoc among men and women, and destruction of land, buildings, crops, plant life, animals and species. Above all they degrade the global environment of both the victor and the vanquished in a way which was previously unheard of. Wider damage came from the world wars of the 20th century than had ever been seen before, when chemical, germ warfare and nuclear weapons of mass destruction were delivered by air, land and sea. These weapons of modern technology not only hit their targets but spread pollution far and wide, on land, in the waters and in the atmosphere. Recent wars in Afghanistan, Vietnam, Cambodia, Palestine, Iran, Iraq, Indo-Pakistan, African countries, South America and European countries did not use atomic weapons but instead heavy explosives and chemical weapons were very common. The devastating destruction of human beings, materials, forests, vegetation and species are of no significance to the warring parties; victory is their only objective. In this process the vanquished are invariably blamed but the victors are no less responsible for the enormous damage done, degrading the local and global environment.

All modern wars, local or global, kill human beings, drain natural resources, enrich munitions manufacturers and warmongers, denude lands of all developments achieved in the agricultural or industrial sectors, uproot communication links, and corrupt the military and civil administrations. The environment is damaged to the core by toxic gases and explosives, and humans suffer from insanitary conditions, undernourishment, disease and there is pollution of land, air and water with, in addition, serious erosion of moral and ethical values widely taking place. Go to any war-ravaged country of the East or West and see for yourself the devastation and suffering the opposing parties cause each other and the environment.[44]

Jane's Intelligence Review, London, in its November 1994 issue reports that even small Israel has seven nuclear installations within her territory in the Middle East. These have been located in Dimona, Soreq, Yodefat, Eilabun, Beere Yakov, Kefar Zakarya and Palmakin. With whose support and connivance these were built is well known. Everywhere in the world this war lust continues unabated at the cost of our precious belongings, physical, intellectual, spiritual and moral. Wars are fought invariably on any good excuse but the grave consequences that ensue can hardly ever justify the excuse unless it is justly and truly done for the cause of the Sovereign Lord or self-defence.[19-20]

The cost incurred by the nations according to one estimate of UNEP is that over the past twenty years, global military expenditure totalled US $17,000,000,000,000, the equivalent of US $1.6 million a minute. During the 1990s military spending in the developed countries began to be reduced slightly – perhaps as a result of a thaw in the Cold War – but defence spending in developing countries increased, notably in the Middle East and Africa. This is only the visible military expenditure but the invisible part may be more costly, and that is how there is plenty and abundance in one part of the globe and poverty in another. Of course, the environment is the biggest casualty of war and violence, which hardly anyone noticed before.[10]

Yet, even here we encounter the mean hand of finance and bankism, for weaponry and arms are one of the most extraordinary markets in the world today, and a quite serious political viewpoint is that modern wars, and the highly profitable rebuilding afterwards, are merely economic events, intrinsic parts of the free-market economy. The massive damage done by these military expenditures are also somehow invisible when it comes to national debts and global pollution. The huge resources used for research and development for military products are not always shown in military expenditure. When a million stomachs are un-fed, a million backs are unclad and millions more are without shelter or medicine, this expenditure sounds criminal or lunatic but that is how we behave without moral and ethical guidance. A chart in *Vital Signs* shows the steady increase in global military expenditure over $1000 billion from 1985-88. (See Appendix 10).

After the devastating war in Kuwait and Iraq, 613 oil wells were ignited by retreating Iraqi forces in Kuwait in 1991. This not only raised damaging fires and clouds of smoke, but it also caused chemical clouds and rain, with resulting fatalities for birds, animals and fish, and human respiratory problems all around.[56]

Cluster bombs and Napalm in Vietnam, chemical bombs in the World Wars and local wars, and the atomic bombs in Japan not only killed people and damaged valuable assets immediately, but they all caused lasting damage in degradation of the global environment. Even the problems of the injured, refugees and homeless are not solved instantly in the land of the victor or victims. Don't we have to care both for today and also for our unborn generations? How can we do that by producing and selling devastating war machines, sacrificing moral and ethical human values, and not following the prompting of human conscience which cries against the monstrousness of modern war and war machines? Can the balance of the clean environment and peace in the world be achieved by lip-service to the 'new world order' or a 'Marxist Utopia'?[57]

3.7. Smoking, Drinking and Drugs

Smoking

Most people in the developed countries now realise that smoking is not only a cause of disease and ill health but also of many deaths, although people in undeveloped countries are surprisingly unaware of this. In Britain lung cancers and heart attacks are the two main killer diseases and smoking is one of their causes. Of course this applies in other countries as well. Smoking is an addiction, like intoxicating drink and drugs, which not only affects the smoker but also damages the environment. Through the powerful tobacco lobby and media support the big tobacco manufacturers dismiss the bad effects of smoking. They enlist or patronise not only physicians but also political leaders and parties to promote their business.

Governments and authorities in Europe and America are taking steps to stop smoking in public, and have legislated for the display of health warnings on manufactured products. Poor Eastern countries are not yet so alarmed, though poor quality tobacco is more common in those regions, with the decreased use of the hubbly bubbly. About 40% to 50% of men and women are addicted to smoking, including smoking marijuana, though the percentage is estimated to be higher in Europe and America. Everyday we receive more information about the health hazards of smoking, even the unborn child in the mother's womb is affected by her nicotine intake. Carbon monoxide and nicotine are the two significant substances in tobacco which affect the heart. Filter cigarettes and hubbly bubbly smoking are sometimes wrongly held to be less injurious for the human metabolism. A chart of rising cigarette smoking is shown in Appendix 11 to indicate the increased risk of pollution by active and passive smoking, causing injurious health hazards. Medical analysis shows that nicotine stimulates the body to produce adrenaline, making the heart beat faster and raising blood pressure. Carbon monoxide joins onto haemoglobin, the red pigment of the blood, reducing its power to carry oxygen to the heart. Jointly they increase the risk of blood clotting (thrombosis) to twice that of non-smokers.[58]

In the countryside of the most populous countries, like China, India, Indonesia and Bangladesh, I have myself seen that they use the hubbly bubbly more because of tradition. This tradition may be considered by some less harmful but yet it is full of hazards. Carbon monoxide, tar and nicotine in tobacco cause lung cancer. Doctors detected these injurious substances in tobacco some time ago. But Muslim jurists and scientists treated smoking as injurious to health and morals centuries ago. Some Muslim jurists consider smoking as a prohibited habit. None of the prophets of Allah were known to be smokers though it was an ancient habit of man. Besides individual health hazards, smoking nicotine, dirt, fume and smell pollute the environment immensely, for which smoking is banned in public places in Saudi Arabia and other countries.

One of my neighbours serving in the British Indian Army during World War II was a chain smoker. He narrated that the cause of his dismissal was an accidental fire in an arms depot, ignited by his cigarette butt. The damage was quite heavy including a few lives, huge amounts of ammunition and other valuables, he used to tell us. What he could not narrate was that he also died of lung cancer and phthisis as reported by the doctors in his death certificate. We witnessed his long suffering along with his family. This is just one example out of millions more. A recent study of the KAA University found that even 'shisha' (hubbly bubbly) smoking, which is very common among the Arabs, is just as injurious as other types of smoking.[59] There are various ayat in the Qur'an, and Traditions of the Prophet Muhammad, salla'llahu 'alaihi wa sallam, asking the faithful not to kill, destroy and hurt others or themselves:

Allah, exalted is He, says:

"Don't kill or destroy yourselves for verily Allah has been to you most merciful."
(Qur'an 4: 26-29)

In one hadith the Messenger of Allah, salla'llahu 'alihi wa sallam, is reported to have said:

"Do not hurt yourselves or injure others."

Waste is strictly prohibited in the Qur'an. (Qur'an 17: 26-7). The economic and other gains achieved through growing, manufacturing, buying and selling, smoking, chewing or snuffing tobacco are totally offset by the health, social and environmental hazards it creates in your location and in the neighbourhood for all, young and old. It is a duty upon all of us, whether we are environmental activists or not, to wake up to our responsibilities and keep the environment clean and unpolluted. It is good that some countries have already initiated non-smoking areas in public transport and places of public gathering by law. Trains, buses, aircraft, cinemas and congregations are thereby saved from both direct and passive smoking pollution. Our youth especially should be saved from this poisonous addiction. Smoking marijuana must not be treated as quite so injurious to the health, but it, in its way, is deadly too. It has a severely deleterious effect in the long term on people's memory, concentration and ability to think.

Though all religions don't consider smoking or drinking as objectionable habits, indeed some regard them as meritorious during their religious and social festivals, such as Hindu 'puja' and Christian mass, nevertheless, they cannot deny their addictive and poisonous effects on body, mind and environment. We should all combine on commonsensical grounds to combat smoking and drinking habits both among the young and adults. When drinking was banned by law in USA, people only obeyed it by force, so the law was withdrawn. Indeed, alcohol sales rose astronomically in that period and the foundations for many a fortune were laid. But most of the Muslims all over the world do obey that law because for the Muslim it is not any man's law but Allah's, and even today refrain from drinking and smoking in unquestioning obedience to the revelation and to the custom and practice of the Prophet, salla'llahu 'alaihi wa sallam, and his companions, radiya'llahu 'anhum, and the later right-acting generations.

Drink and Drugs

There is considerable evidence that alcoholic drinks and perhaps some drugs were permitted to be consumed in very tiny quantities in the older spiritual traditions of man. For example, even as late as the time of 'Isa, 'alaihi's-salam, the Children of Israel were still permitted to drink a little grape juice which had fermented slightly, and which they called wine. However, it has been said that with the coming of Islam, Allah ta'ala knew that an age was coming where the consumption of intoxicants would be far vaster than ever in the history of humanity, and that would lead to our present epoch when industries would turn out huge volumes of powerfully alcoholic drinks, and so in the revelation of Islam alcohol and intoxicants are prohibited absolutely and finally, and Allah knows best. Tawhid is not for a time or for a people, but for all times that have been and to come for all mankind, however the shari'ah at any particular time is shaped and adapted to fit the conditions of the time. The shari'ah of Islam is unique in that it is for all peoples on the earth until the end of time. Allah ta'ala says:

"O you who believe, intoxicants and gambling, sacrifice to stones, and (divination by) arrows,

are an abomination, of shaytan's handiwork: so give up such (abomination), that you may prosper."
(Qur'an 5: 90 and see also 2: 219)

Man, by a misuse of his intellect or in the pride of his scientific achievements, sometimes loses his balance. But the Divinity reveals His own glory in time and man sees it sometimes in pain and sometimes in grace. We are surely watching the environmental catastrophe in pain. If we can re-establish the environmental balance, which has been grossly degraded by human actions, we are likely to see the return of that grace. That can only happen with a return of obedience to Allah and His Messengers, and that will never be complete for anybody unless it is submission to the Last of the Messengers, Muhammad, salla'llahu 'alaihi wa sallam. Yet, Allah in his mercy, allows peoples of the Book to remain within their own traditions, as long as governance is in the hands of the Muslims. We have seen that condition of the Dar al-Islam lapse, and now we have seen the horrors that the non-believers have heaped on the world, including their devastation of the ecosystem, through their disobedience of Allah and His Messengers. As man we can only with all seriousness turn back to Allah, and summon mankind to do so, leaving the final result in His hands.

Considering the effects of intoxication by alcoholic drinks and drugs, we see that even a healthy addict is not allowed to drive a car or fly a plane. A drunken one is not allowed to be in a place of work or worship, in any religion or law. The reason is not only that a drunk loses his mental, moral and physical balance, but the use of alcohol or drugs also invites incurable disease, and loss of potency and mental balance. Look at a drugged person who can neither afford his drugs nor give them up, leading him to the door of dishonour, disease, criminality, violence and death. In the countries of Europe, America and elsewhere the drug barons are not only spreading the pollution but also ruining the law and order of a peaceful society. So all sane persons should give up the habit of drinks and drugs for physical, spiritual and environmental reasons.

3.8 The Population Explosion

It is estimated that, at the present rate, the world population will rise by approximately another two billions over the current five billions in the next twenty years. The birthrate is higher in the developing countries and so is infant mortality. In some of the developed countries of Europe, the birthrate is falling, as if the living don't want to share their prosperity with the unborn. Maybe environmental pollution has reduced fertility. Perhaps they no longer realise that quality of life is dependent more on a contented family life than on an ill-gotten mountain of prosperity. A balanced economic life is interlinked with social and moral values.

The problem is not with the numbers but with the disparity between the numbers – rich and poor, it is equity and disparity that make things moral or immoral. Some of us consume and waste resources at the cost of others. The developing countries, with over 75% of world population, earn and consume less than 25% of the world income. Population explosion is a bigger problem for the world's poor, and yet it is also a huge problem for the apparently prosperous ones. 'Birth control' came but without due respect for moral and humanitarian values, as a mere matter of convenience for consumers who didn't want to have to share life and provisions with a new person.

Some ecologists consider the population explosion as a factor of environmental degradation following the "optimum population" theory of Thomas Malthus (1798). His theory was very popular in the post revolution period of France but its popularity proved inconstant during the following decades. Even Karl Marx labelled his theory as a "libel on the human race", since he regarded overpopulation not as an outcome of nature but of the laws of capitalism, the outcome of disparity. Darwin's theory of the survival of the fittest and his theory of evolution may apply to the historical growth of animals, minerals or vegetables but applying it to human creation is another libel against the laws and orders of the Creator. There are still strong supporters of Malthusian, Marxist and Darwinian theories, but surplus food production on a global basis negated these concepts in the subsequent world situation. Over the last two centuries, world food production has coped well with increased population. Modern bio-technology promises more. Production of wheat, rice, meat, fish, milk, butter and other food products increased faster than the population explosion. The figures for fish and meat production between 1950-1990, in Appendices 12 and 13, show the increase.

Any shortage is in terms of distribution, not production. While the people in underdeveloped countries die of hunger and vitamin deficiency, the huge surplus in Europe and America is dumped in stores, or caves or ploughed back into the earth or dumped at sea (wheat, butter, oranges, etc.) only to keep their markets and prices stable. While some people are overfed causing heart and other disease, other people cry for food and go to their death while there is plenty of it available in human hands elsewhere. The USDA chart shows the rise of world grain production from 1950-90 (from *Vital Signs*). The same was the position of meat and fish, as shown in Appendices 12 and 13 above.

Family planning by abortion, legalised sodomy and 'gay' life, sex with contraceptives outside marriage and other amoral practices are pursuits which result in population control, and paradoxically in the serious counter problem in the West, an ageing population. Actually moral and healthy family development, following the divine code, is essential for all of us and it does not prohibit but guides some forms of birth control. It is human inequity and moral degradation, not just the population explosion, that cause food and resource scarcity. You have to conserve and share the gifts of the Lord, not pollute and destroy them.

Man spreads the *fasad* (corruption) of inequaty, exploitation and profiteering, though our Lord has provided food and drink in due proportion to every living being born or yet to be born. The Lord Who caters for the food and nourishment of the foetuses in the wombs of mothers also caters for their subsistence till death be that creature a human, animal or any other species. Man has to toil for it with justice and equity and not with mischief. Paul Harrison discusses this subject in his book *The Third Revolution* with the conclusion that we have to work for "a sustainable balance with our natural environment". Overcrowded and dirty cities and slums, with poor health and hygiene, and addictive and intoxicating drink and drugs no doubt damage the environment but it is more due to sociopolitical maladministration than population explosion.[60]

Evangelical writer Loren Wilkinson writes:

> "A child born into an average American family will use up to fifty times as many of the earth's goods – and leave at least that much more in waste – as a child born into a poor family in the developing world."[86]

In 1963 when we were the guests of Chinese government in Peking the then premier Chou en Lai posed a question on this topic of population explosion over the lunch hosted by him in the Peoples Hall to the delegation of Pakistan: "Are we born with one hungry stomach or also with two robust hands?"

In the name of birth control for the purpose of a happy family, the West is spreading free sex with free abortion, celibacy with sodomy and breaking up the family by moral degradation. Society is polluted with sex scandals and socio-cultural unhappiness. Being drunk with material pleasure and prosperity, man is not fulfilling his covenant and the trust of his Lord. Do we have to wait for the fate of the people who disobeyed Lut, 'alaihi's-salam, who are mentioned in the Books so many times?

The Qur'an mentioned the event in more than a dozen ayat to underline the divine warning. To the dismal disregard of truth and morality, the UN Plan of Action of 1994 on population growth was rubber stamped in Cairo by the same misguided charlatans who boast of the capitalist free market and communist bonded Utopia. The Plan, of $34,000,000,000 US, was opposed by both the Roman Catholics and Muslims as it would support and encourage murder through abortion, immorality through freely available contraception thus facilitating sex outside of marriage, and family disintegration; if we were minded to see these things in terms of a conspiracy we would have to count this as a subtle plan to further degrade the environment – in this case the social environment – of the developing countries as well.

The authors of *Imperilled Planet* write,

> "If every citizen in the world were to reach the same standard of living as in the North, the stress placed on the environment would be intolerable. Attempting to solve the population explosion through increased per capita income – and hence increased consumption – can only increase the impact of people on their environment. It is therefore self defeating."

When we talk of development only, with no regard for the environment, or with regard just for the environment without any for social values, we only end up with self-defeating results. An additional person in a family, including a baby, in an industrial country, consumes far more and places far greater pressure on natural resources than an additional person in the Third World. The US with about 5% of the global population is responsible for some 24% of global CO_2 emissions. It is not just the population explosion rather it is the social erosion which has to be contained in order to prevent ecological degradation. 'Ends justify the means' is neither socially nor legally correct for the environment or for sustainable development. Allah ta'ala says in the Qur'an:

> **"Join not anything with Him, be good to your parents, kill not your children on a plea of want; We provide sustenance for you and for them; come not near to indecent deeds whether open or secret; take not life, which Allah has made sacred except by way of justice and law. Thus does He command you that you may learn wisdom."**
> (Qur'an 6: 151)

The population growth rates of the industrial nations are closer to stabilising but their consumption rate is much higher per capita than sustainable capacity. The ecological emphasis today is on population control by fair means or foul. But what about consumption control and what about global population and income distribution? It is an intrinsic part of the shari'ah and one of its pillars that the Khalifah and those in authority must take the zakat from the net wealth of the Muslims – not from their income – and distribute it among the categories of the poor and needy, etc.

These are not taxes imposed by a state, but they are part of the revelation of Allah. It is not in any way demanded that there be equality of wealth but it is a fundamental pillar of Islam that there is some redistribution of wealth.

The world is producing enough food and goods but the majority of the population is suffering from their unjust and inequitable distribution. The other main reason for our ecological and economic suffering is the habit of over consumption with its concomitant waste. Is it not a punishable wrong action?

Thus our environmental programme on population should be:

A. Production and consumption control without waste or pollution;

B. Equitable distribution of population and income worldwide, through migration and the re-application of the zakah;

C. Family bonds and planning with socio-moral concern, and;

D. Honest simple living with sex between men and their wives.

Thinly populated countries like Canada, the USA, Australia, Arabia and Russia could accommodate more population from the overcrowded regions. But that is a matter that does not require central planning for the world's poor have already thought about it and are heading in unstoppable droves across the world's borders into these spheres of affluence. The throwaway and surplus wealth of the prosperous can economically and socially be shared with others. Guard against all waste, be it of food, drink, clothes, money or lifestyle. Let us orient ourselves for simple and honest living without creating extravagant needs for ourselves and our children. Family planning on a social basis, not on the basis of convenience and economics, must be integrated with family bonds of love and affection. Educational programmes to treat sex not only as a sensual animal pleasure but as a joyous expression of marital love. The multi-billion dollar expenditure planned on coercive unethical birth control in the Rio, Cairo and Peking summits would be better spent on promoting these four objectives for a better environment and a better world. The defence expenditure of all countries could easily be reduced since it is clear that the nation-state is increasingly an anachronism in this age and that armaments for defence are merely a super-market sustained by defence scares and bogey-men like Hitler and Stalin. If it were globally taxed by at least 5% per annum the market is so huge that the income from it would mean that there would not be a problem of sustainable development or a lack of a pollution control fund. However, whether ethically minded ecologists would want funding from such a source is a moot point.

3.9. Unethical Acts

The industrially developed countries hardly use any moral or ethical standards for exploitation of natural resources; the profit motive is their primary goal. They built empires, possessed colonies, obtained labour by slavery or low wages, recklessly burnt fossil fuels creating pollution on soil, water and atmosphere, created shanty towns with few facilities of health and recreation, dumped natural and chemical wastes on land and water and built up communication and industrial networks which generated enormous amounts of all-round pollution.

It took seventy years for communism's utopian mistake to become glaringly apparent to all, although their underlying assumptions about the Creator and His creation have never been questioned by most people and are now almost established in popular imagination as unassailable facts. It took two centuries for capitalism's capital folly of polluting the environment to emerge clearly and unequivocally into the light. The industrial revolution gave birth to both materialistic capitalism and authoritarian communism, both holding out sweet promises of development and prosperity for mankind in terms of GDP and GNP. But what we have received in return is an environmental time bomb ready to explode the earth and its inhabitants.

We have seen so far that all the three natural gifts of the creation – land, water and air – are seriously polluted by various known and unknown activities of mankind. Pollution has reached a catastrophic stage, so if not URGENTLY stopped it may bring total collapse for everything and every being on our planet Earth.

We do not know whether a Nuh's ark will be available to save some of the species or not. Some ecologists predict that there are only a few years left but others predict some decades in which we have a chance to save the situation. Either way, if we don't move fast to improve the already lost balance in the natural global environment we are very soon in trouble.

Before we can resolve to act we have to understand the cardinal truth. In spite of philosophical, political and scientific differences of opinion on creation there seems to be no plausible doubt that nature itself is based on certain established rules and on an order. We can call it a discipline or balance not only of the earth but of the whole universe. This balance, admitted by all, existed for millions of years but did not exist in isolation or accident. As the very existence of the universe is an indication of the One Who brought it into existence, the intricate order and balance of the creation is an indication of the infinite knowledge of the Creator and His power over His vast creation. By denying this truth we have only created material prosperity of a short duration, for example, the wealth brought about by imperial conquests, the industrial revolution, the communist would-be utopia, and the cyber-wealth of the age of space travel and of the technology era. But the clear signs (*ayat*) of the Supreme will bring us back to the sure divine guidance of the *deen* which encompasses all aspects of human endeavour, the social, intellectual, spiritual, legal, scientific, commercial, and the so neglected ethical. See the various publications of the International Society of Environmental Ethics for an in depth study.[89]

To decipher the signs of the Supreme, the ayat of the Noble Qur'an, those of us who are not Muslims may examine the teachings of the major religions of the world and their environmental guidance, if any, and see that Islam is a confirmation of all that is best in them and clearly the re-expression for this age of the essential teachings of all the Prophets in a new and fresh manner for a global age. This exploration is meant to bring out that true guidance which was the contribution of the Prophets, and it is not to criticise any of the Prophets.

We the inhabitants of the earth, animate and inanimate, however intelligent or dumb we may be are only minutest particles of the vast universe. The earth is only one of the known nine planets in our solar system. It is perhaps one of many such solar systems in the universe, although this is not yet proved. The sun belongs to a family of stars and because of its nearness to the planet earth (150 million kilometres) it looks big to us, but there are other bigger suns and stars in the universe round whom it is suggested other planets and moons move, although these have not yet been observed. As the sun travels through space – a vast void – it takes all its planets and asteroids with it orbiting in a fixed order constrained by gravity. Solar gravity keeps the planets in their orbits. For millions of years an order has been meticulously maintained by a force superior to tiny man, and superior even to the earth and the vast stars. (Qur'an 37: 5, 27: 88, 21: 30, 15: 19)

A monkey on a computer could possibly create sound but it would not be music, but a mindless accident cannot assemble a computer chip, not to speak of a planet or the universe. The nearest planets – Mercury (58 million km away) – and the farthest – Pluto (5,930 million km away) – and the other seven planets and all their moons and asteroids move around the sun in a faultless dynamic balance. Only the planet Earth is known to have living beings: men, animals, birds, fishes, plants and species.

Allah mentions jinn and angels as living beings of His creation in the Qur'an. Jinn are made of fire and they may inhabit the earth like the fire does. Other planets may also contain life, even if only in the form of simple cellular forms or bacteria, so scientists are now hopefully probing Mars and other planets, and exploring the depths of space through the Hubble telescope and other satellites equipped with astronomical equipment. Stars and planets are neither born accidentally nor do they live permanently, so they all follow a common path of life and death. Nothing else, from the tiniest quark or sub-atomic particle to the largest quasars and super-galaxies, is permanent or eternal like Him. They are all different in life-span, form and nature but all are interrelated in the dynamic ordering of the cosmos. This order comes from an Infinite, Omnipotent Omnipresent Power Whom man calls by various names. But He is none but the ultimate Sovereign Creator. Science and technology may not see Him but all living hearts do, as testified to by the accumulated spiritual experience of submitted men, Muslims, from every age and from every corner of the planet. Allah says in the Qur'an:

> **"No vision can grasp Him, but He grasps all vision. He is the Subtle, the Well Aware."**
> (Qur'an 6: 103)

In *Religions and Spiritual Perspective* M.T. Mahdi briefly considered the Islamic contribution to the study of the environment. The Qur'an and the Traditions emphasise again and again the extraordinary nature of Allah's creation and His imposition on us of the 'trust' (*amanah*) and the responsibility to be its custodians (*khalifah*).[62] The UNEP for the first time considered the importance of moral and ethical awareness in *Ethics and Agenda 21*, authored by Dr. N.J. Brown.[64]

This earth's environment is not only under siege from pollution but social and ethical degradation are throttling it to death. No amount of remedial measures can be successful without a social awareness of our responsibilities. None but the people aware of their spiritual responsibilities to their Lord will move to accept this challenge. It is only the people who are aware that they will have to render an account of their actions to their Lord, and the people who are from moment to moment aware that their Lord sees what they do, who will not only live in harmony with the environment, but will also rouse themselves to take on the difficult social and political work that must be done to reverse the damage we are outlining in this book. Those people still exist among the Muslims, and increasingly such people from other communities are finding their place in the Ummah of Islam as they have done throughout history, finding that the only way of remaining true to their Prophets' teachings is within the Ummah of Muhammad, salla'llahu 'alaihi wa sallam. Therefore, seeing that the main culprit in our diagnosis has been the commercial world in all its manifestations, whether in the transformation of warfare into a market force, or the pollution caused by the worldwide industrial nexus, then it is by recovering the teachings of Islam on commercial transactions that we will bring divine guidance to bear on our situation.

First and foremost we must re-invigorate the absolute prohibition of usury, which cannot be done merely as a negative but only by recreating anew the practices of Muslim commerce with an interest-free financial system. Then we must revive the pillar of zakah, which cannot happen until the Muslims' commerce has been purified since zakah is unacceptable from haram wealth. The restitution of the zakah can resolve many of the economic and social ills of the Ummah including those of the ecology.

Theologians or Technocrats?

Everyone follows some religion. Indeed there is no more religious activity in the world today than the 'modernist' philosophy whose parts are 'development', 'progress' and 'liberal democracy', etc., except that this cult is anything but 'unitarian' in nature – it is clearly polytheistic. We can explore their perspective on how and why we are faced with this environmental disaster and how to save mankind from it. Scientists and ecologists, even if occasionally they do theoretically belong to one religion or the other, are almost without exception members of the global cult of modernism. We have to find out from their teachings who can control the collapse, if anyone.

4.1. Judaeo-Christianism

Judaism

In theological terms Judaism purports to be the oldest religion. Adam and Hawwa, 'alaihima's-salam, the first human couple on earth, lived close to the condition of the fitrah, worshipping Allah alone. Ibrahim and Ya'qub, 'alaihima's-salam, were some of the Prophets of tawhid through whom the Children of Israel claimed their descent. The modern Ashkenazi Jew may not do so, since he is descended from Turkic peoples from north of the Caucasus, as demonstrated so ably by scholars from Tel Aviv University. Musa and 'Isa, 'alaihima's-salam, were genuine prophets with revelation from Allah. None of them were either Jews or Christians, but they were Muslims – submitted and surrendered to Allah – following the true way of Allah, i.e. Islam.

Some historians place Hinduism as an older religion of 4,000-5,000 years old. But they cannot determine the age of Adam or Ibrahim, 'alaihima's-salam. The Roman Catholic Church excommunicated their own scientists like Copernicus and Galileo for holding that the earth moves round the sun, contrary to then Aristotelian belief which had become crystallised as Christian dogma. Scientists and historians may err because to err is human.

The illustrious prophets of the Children of Israel, i.e. Musa and Dawud, 'alaihima's-salam, were blessed with revelations from Allah. These revelations are supposed to have been compiled partially in the Bible but, however, long after the demise of the original Tawrah and Zabur. The contents of the old Books poorly remembered were split into pieces, modified and translated and can now be found in the Old Testament of the Bible. These books today contain comments, interpolations and explanations of the rabbis and scholars from over the millennia. Especially important to the Jews of today is the Talmud, which is entirely rabbinical lore, often of a strangely magical and superstitious nature. The human comments, explanations and adaptations, as opposed to the lost divine revelation, are what dominate everything that they claim to be their revealed Books; the originals being lost and distorted.

Judaism believes in the existence of God and in His creation of the material and immaterial world and the universe. The Ten Commandments of the Old Testament, said to be part of that which Allah the Glorious and Exalted directly revealed to Musa, 'alaihi's-salam, on Mount Sinai still form the basis of Jewish moral and social law. They believe in an afterlife but not in original sin; rather they believe in original blessing as the 'original creation was good'. They also believe in man's free will to choose between right and wrong, which is important also for the environmental matters that we are discussing now.

In many respects Judaism and Christianity have notions that they have some kind of unity with Islam, starting from: a common genetic descent of the Prophets, to various codes which govern the personal, familial and social life of right-conduct, and the teaching of the nature of the relationship between the creation and the Creator. If you read the Qur'an – which is preserved unmodified or un-adapted in its original revealed language – and compare it with the other books which have been modified by their adherents, you will find yet that all deal basically with the Creator, the creation, justice, right action and the world hereafter. Deep below you will find a concordance with the teachings of others who were or who may have been Prophets, Zoroaster, the ancient teachers of Hinduism and possibly even the teachings of the Buddha too. However, the Buddha did not talk of a Creator, perhaps because he came among the Hindus who were involved in theological hair-splitting, and so the Buddha maintained what he called the 'Noble Silence'.

The reason for that is that the Hindus have a tradition that is so ancient that it is perhaps one of the most corrupted of all the traditions, and has come to tolerate a thousand idols. When the Buddha was born among them he was unable to find a single enlightened being who could bring him to real knowledge. Instead he found enormous numbers of hair-splitting theologians and an equal number of Yogis who were developing the arts and sciences of control over the body, and meditational practices which gave them a certain power. However, despite all the religiosity there was not a single genuine spiritual teacher in the Buddha's time, and that was 2,500 years ago. If he was a genuine Prophet – and we have nothing directly mentioning him in the Islamic tradition – he may have had a similar position among the Hindus as 'Isa, 'alaihi's-salam, had among the Jews. Those who rejected 'Isa among the Jews were cursed, and Judaism today is the aberrant teaching of rebels against Allah and His Messengers. Similarly with the Buddha, the Hindus who rejected his teaching became almost the most backward of all the religions of the world, putting up an idol to every conceivable object of worship.

Hindus talk about reincarnation in this world, but they took the idea of reincarnation to avoid meaningful action in this life. The Buddha, being born in that culture never challenged the idea of reincarnation since he had adopted the way of the 'Noble Silence' on matters of theology and disputation. However, the Buddha insisted that if reincarnation were true then the fact of being born as a human in this life was perhaps one of the rarest pieces of good fortune and an opportunity which must be seized upon to advance spiritually to full liberation. It was inconceivable to delay anything to another life. Thus subtly he overturned the deadly destructive nature of the belief in reincarnation and transformed it into something much closer to the psychological preparedness of the Muslim to make the most of this one and only life in preparation for the reckoning of the next life.

There are other points of difference between them, but examining whatever is genuine from the teachings of the ancient prophets that might impinge on the ecological field we may find a great similarity prevalent in their faiths, if we must consistently disentangle the genuine teachings of an ancient prophet from the perversions of it practised by his alleged followers in our day.

More significant than the numbers of followers of the religions, is the survival if only partially of fitrah in many parts of the world among peoples of all sorts of diverse creeds and particularly among young people. The net effect of this is that most ordinary people on the earth still retain a simple belief in the Divine, in the Unseen worlds, and in their own accountability. This is something that survives largely in spite of the official religion or lack of it. It is fitrah that Islam is based on. The Messenger of Allah, salla'llahu 'alaihi wa sallam, is reported to have said, "Islam is the deen of fitrah." In an age when the religions have largely ossified into sterile dogmas and rituals, Islam's real appeal to people is its call to the fitrah. It is fitrah, too, that rejects pollution and the tawdry baubles of development and progress, and refuses to accept pollution. Thus it is often the young, who are closest to the fitrah, who are most vocal in opposing pollution. People with more or less fitrah intact are found in practically the whole of the global population, barring many of the over-cultured inhabitants

The Ten Commandments to Musa, 'alaihi's-salam, as we have them transmitted among the Jews and the Christians, speak of rest on the Sabbath day even for the cattle. A Sabbath for rest of the land itself is also prescribed on the seventh year and is known as Shemtta. In their religious services you hear the words – chayim, shabbat and shalom – being repeated time and again. The word 'chayim' means life and this life is for all beings, the creation as a whole. Among the blessings in their prayers a blessing on fruits and vegetables is very common. In the flood of the time of Nuh, 'alaihi's-salam, he was asked to conserve male and female couples of every species in the ark so that they may subsequently carry on with procreation.

According to the Old Testament, Adam was placed in the garden of Eden "to till it and preserve it" Genesis 2: 15. In the story of "the chosen people and the chosen land" of the Jews it is said that the prosperity of the land depends on the obedience of those people to God's covenants. "If you pay heed to the commandments which I give you this day, and love the Lord your God and serve Him with your heart and soul, then I will send rain for your land in season...". It is also said therein not to serve other gods and to take care of the land otherwise "you will soon vanish from the rich land which the Lord is giving you". (Deuteronomy 11: 13-17). Undoubtedly there has been a difference of opinion amongst Christian and Jewish theologians as to the opening chapters of Genesis 1: 28 which calls for "dominion" of man over the earth. As this "dominion" took the shape of "domination" by many of the Christian countries of the West in different forms of imperialism and colonisation, the blame went to the Bible and its followers.

The role of Judaism in the nature of colonisation, exploitation and violation of covenants was a story only of ancient history. However, modern 'Israel' has a long implication in the history of usury and the rise of banking, which are themselves the entire motor of the industrial and militentary complex that has wreaked the devastation of the environment. That ecological destruction was bad enough, even if we did not mention the complete breakdown in the social fabric of society occasioned by the insane rush to pay escalating bills and to join the stampede to secure fantasy wealth, which is of a much more serious significance than even the dreadful vanishing of species. If humanness vanishes then the human species, for which the cosmos was created, is as good as dead.

Then Israel as a Zionist entity, and as a nation-state, entered the fold of blame-worthiness in the Middle East. Their record of Zionist practices in Israel has not only been controversial but reprehensible, acts of land usurpation and human rights violation, and of domination and exploitation. Norman Solomon points out in *Judaism and Ecology*, pp. 27:

> "The context of Genesis 1: 28 is indeed that of humans being made in the image of God, the beneficent Creator of good things, its meaning is therefore very precise, that humans being in the image of God, are summoned to share in His creative work, and to do all in their power to sustain creation".

Even in war Jews, as Muslims, are 'not to destroy the trees' (Deuteronomy 20: 19).

Jewish traditions have taken wider conservation measures through its festivals and practices than its Books could inspire. Rituals they may be, but one can notice their importance in agricultural festivals, pilgrimages, Shevat and other festivals which encourage conservation and management of the environment. To plant a cedar sapling on the birth of a boy and planting a cypress sapling on the birth of a girl is a potentially good environmental tradition that still goes on in some Jewish community. And Tu Bi Shevat, a new year festival for trees is also a tradition that is widely observed. Because of compassion for animals, some Jews also follow a vegetarian life based on some biblical reference. Eating flesh and fish are not prohibited in Judaism but blood is. Except in the remote traditions of the later rabbis or recent interpretations of some verses of Old Testament, any direct legal reference from the Old Testament is not available on the pollution of air or water. Though some renowned Jewish scientists have propounded the theory of Evolution, as did Darwin, they do not have any biblical support.

The incessant bombings and occupation of neighbouring lands, their trigger-happiness and readiness to destroy the 'intifida', their suppression of Palestinian human rights, and the nuclear arsenals of Israel are earning no laurels for Judaism as a religion or as environmental activists. We may have to try and keep the present day, extreme Zionism of Israel and the Jews as being something different from the revelations of the now largely lost Tawrah and Zabur.

In Israel a lot of environmental laws and regulations are in force today in response to global ecological degradation. Everyone is coming to realise that today's environmental catastrophe is worse than almost any other disaster known in history. So every person must act and act unitedly.

For a common human action on the causes of pollution, the only point of concordance between the Muslims and people of other traditions is submission to the Divine and obedience to the Prophets. Let the Jews join us in the brotherhood of Islam by accepting a true tawhid and the Messengership of Muhammad, salla'llahu 'alaihi wa sallam. If they refuse that, then let them be true to the revelations of their Prophets, 'alaihimu's-salam.

Environmental catastrophe is a global one crossing all frontiers of geography, economy, politics and religion. Zionists, being largely secularists and atheists, may evade their religious and environmental responsibilities but the Jews cannot. So they have to collaborate with other faiths, and the only way to do that is to be true to their own revelations, following their Book, the Tawrah, in every way and, for our purposes here, in the field of environment. They may not have a comprehensive method of control with them but they can collaborate with other people, burying some of their misgivings and animosity.

Rabbi Arthur Hertzberg in the Assisi Declaration writes:

> "Now, when the whole world is in peril, when the environment is in danger of being poisoned and various species, both plant and animal, are becoming extinct, it is our Jewish responsibility to put the defence of the whole of nature at the very centre of our concern."[53]

Christianity

Christianity is only 2,000 years old but its nominal followers outnumber by a slight degree the Muslims and to a much greater degree followers of any other religion, old or new. When we talk of theological influence and counting of heads for the environment they are the ones most involved and they are the ones who can most degrade or improve the global environment. That is especially so considering that the whole usurious banking mechanism and industrial complex that have devastated the environment were created and came to power in so-called Christian lands.

'Isa, 'alaihi's-salam, was – according to the slightly unreliable Christian sources – born in Nazareth with date trees around, near the city of Jerusalem. And a man made of 'clay' in such an environment could not be far away from fitrah.

During his short life time of approximately thirty-two years, he not only worked for the salvation of man but displayed his kindness to animals, plants and all creatures. His stories describing the 'Kingdom of God', as narrated in Matthew, Luke and Mark, are mostly set against farming or fishing backgrounds. Allah showed miracles by means of him. He was not a god but a prophet to guide man with the message of Allah.

Various sects of Christians depict 'Isa, 'alaihi's-salam, differently no doubt, but we are not entering into that sterile debate of theology here but trying to find the interrelationship of the creation and its creatures through revelation. Christians being a once dominant global force – a role now ceded to their natural successors, liberal secularists – and in spite of their past shaky role in the environment, we have to summon also to establish the teachings of their Prophet, however imperfectly recorded in their books. In order to approach that they need to re-examine afresh, as many authors are doing, the role of Paul in creating what is idenitifiably modern Christianity as opposed to the real teachings of 'Isa, 'alaihi's-salam. How could true followers of the man who so totally renounced the world and so devastatingly challenged his contemporaries to do the same, how could his true followers devastate the planet out of plain greed? It is not possible; it was the followers of the pseudo-religion created by Paul who did that.

'Isa, 'alaihi's-salam, was born a being of tawhid like other prophets and indeed like every person born. The Prophet Muhammad, salla'llahu 'alaihi wa sallam, said that "Every creature born is born on the fitrah". He tried to guide the Jews who had gone away from the true path of tawhid, but they rejected him and may have tried to have him crucified, an undertaking in which they failed.

Muslims accept 'Isa, 'alaihi's-salam, as one of their prophets who had the Book the Injil (wrongly translated as the Gospel, since the Gospels may only contain fragments of that lost revelation) revealed to him as the Tawrah was revealed to the prophet Musa and the Zabur to the prophet Dawud, 'alaihima's-salam. These prophets and the other prophets of God were commissioned to teach the unitary knowledge called tawhid and to instruct people in the revealed law for mankind, the shari'ah, the totality of which is Islam. Islam – submission and surrender to Allah – is and has been the revealed way for all of mankind starting from Adam, 'alaihi's-salam, and continuing through Ibrahim to Musa and 'Isa, 'alaihimu's-salam, and completed by Allah in His last Book, the Noble Qur'an, and the last Prophet Muhammad, salla'llahu 'alaihi wa sallam; the one and the same religion, not three.

Human egoism, pride, prejudice and love of power and pleasure made the later Christians change the original message of the unity of Allah and the command to worship Him alone. Their scholars, priests and popes modified important laws and narrations from the revealed books, viz. the unity of Allah, the coming of the Prophet named Ahmad (the true Greek "Periqlytos – Illustrious and Praised" possibly being mistranscribed as "Paraclytos – comforter" and thus leading to the modern version "Paraclete"). They ignored the prohibition of blood, pig-meat, alcohol and of giving and taking interest and increasingly came to forget the command to show compassion to all creatures without brutal mastery. This the Paulines did for their self-interest and to placate the ruling authorities. The authentic followers of 'Isa, 'alaihi's-salam, believe in the creation of the world by the Creator. Man was created 'in His image', and He, exalted is He, said "Be!" to everything and things and beings were there. According to that original revelation it was neither through 'evolution' that man appeared nor through an accidental 'big bang' that the universe came into existence. While creating man, the first couple being Adam and Hawwa, 'alaihima's-salam, willpower was given them to decide between right and wrong and the resulting consequences of reward or punishment in the Garden or in the Fire. So man is a superior being with intelligence and responsibility for his own acts; this applies to all acts of environmental pollution.

Adam and Hawwa, 'alaihima's-salam, fell from heaven through their wrong. That 'Isa, 'alaihi's-salam, came to the earth to remove that 'original sin' by his sacrifice on the cross was introduced authoritatively into the New Testament only in the 4th century CE. Even the New Testament was not entirely recorded until between 90 and 200 years after the disappearance of 'Isa, 'alaihi's-salam. The Bible itself, in its two divisions of Old Testament and New Testament, is not the original revelations to those great prophets but the narrations, explanations, translations and interpretations of its followers and theologians recorded through different languages and revisions.

Today's Bible is a series of books written by many human authors over hundreds of years and still being revised, modified and edited by its followers. You may refer to any introduction to a modern Bible to verify this fact. The original Hebrew and Aramaic texts of revelations are not available, and indeed not even traceable today. 'Isa, 'alaihi's-salam, was first doctrinally betrayed in 325 A.D at the Council of Nicaea, organised and presided over by the then pagan Roman Emperor Constantine to settle the destabilising theological disputes among his Christian subjects and thus consolidate his empire. The then Christian scholars in Alexandria and Jerusalem differed on adapting the Bible to royal patronage but gradually found it convenient for the elevation of Christianity to a position of definite political power within the secular and pagan Roman Empire. They had to accept the incorporation of many Roman customs and practices into Christianity. The Greek Orthodox church, the Protestants and many other denominations of Christianity since have come to differ on the modified Bible, and go in for making new and improved editions everyday.

Approximately 600 years after the disappearance of 'Isa, 'alaihi's-salam, Muhammad, salla'llahu 'alaihi wa sallam, was commissioned as the Last Prophet and Messenger to receive the true revelations of Allah for the complete guidance of all mankind until the end of time. These final revelations are preserved without any modifications in the Noble and Glorious Qur'an, and will remain so to guide erring humans forever. Similarly, the complement to that, the Sunnah or practice of the Messenger of Allah, salla'llahu 'alaihi wa sallam, and of his Khulafa who took the right way, is still with us too, preserved as is no other Sunnah of any other prophet.

According to Genesis the Lord took Adam, 'alaihi's-salam, "and put him into the garden of Eden to dress it and to keep it". And out of the ground He also "formed every beast of the field and every fowl of the air and brought them unto Adam". The biblical 'dominion' over things and beings on the earth given to man was used by the Christians, first by the Roman church and then later it was given a new life in Protestant interpretations, as authority for 'domination' and exploitation. After the industrial revolution in Europe this spirit of domination led them to colonise and exploit the natural resources of the East and the West until this day. The nearness to fitrah once embodied in their revelation was flouted by their imperial powers in the name of 'civilising' the natives of Asia, Africa, Australasia and America. In addition to their superior force and mechanical know-how they utilised missionaries to consolidate their imperial gains and to open the way to exploit the natural resources of forests, foods and minerals.

Men, animals, birds and species were not spared by them at home or abroad. The problems of drought, famine, flood, vanishing forests, loss of topsoil, desertification, global warming, the pollution of rivers, seas, land and air, acid-rain, the hole in the ozone layer, nuclear fallout, plagues, cancers and other disasters didn't arise in a day or even a decade. These are not all natural disasters but are mostly man-made, and humans have to address their solution not only physically and materially, but with a moral and true spiritual awakening.

As a major religion Christianity has a major responsibility, perhaps historically THE major responsibility, if we discount the role of the Jews in monetarism, banking and high finance. Modern environmentalists, most of whom are historically Christians, received their inspiration to save the environment from its devastation not so much from the Bible but from 20th century science and 19th century European romanticism. The stories of the Bible repeated that if people went their own way flouting God's order, evil results would follow, not only for the humans but also in the rest of the creation. The earth would suffer from human folly and lose its productiveness, as indicated in the books of Job, for example.

Barnabas was a trusted companion of 'Isa, 'alaihi's-salam, who is known to have recorded his sayings. Later

Roman Christians banished his record in order to give prominence to Paul's views of Christianity. Paul was an enemy of the Disciples who had turned Christian without meeting 'Isa, 'alaihi's-salam. Later thinkers who followed in his tradition, like Augustine and Boethius, went even further away from fitrah and emphasised a spiritual existence in the kingdom of God. The same was the trend of the Puritans and Calvinists in Europe, based on the verses of the Bible which command 'to multiply and dominate the earth'. This added impetus to capitalism, industrial-cum-imperial autocracy and secularism. Marxism appeared as the ultimate product of the conflict between different churches in which different denominations fought each other more than concentrating on their devotion to God and His laws. Development and material prosperity became the target of the Christian world ruling the West and East. That imperial and industrial prosperity has taken us all to the doors of environmental doom today.

The rise of Protestantism in the 16th century in Germany and other parts of Europe through Martin Luther and John Calvin was a revolt against Roman Catholicism and its corrupt priesthood. Protestants stood for direct communion with God without the mediation of priests and they also stood for the material wellbeing of man. This sense of the piety of hard work and material gain, based on a reading of Genesis, was taken to America, Asia and Africa by settlers and missionaries. Material development and prosperity at any cost were taken as signs of God's blessings and propagated as such and are still so taken even today in America by tele-evangelists and others. Exploiting the land, forest and mines of the colonies was done on the basis of Genesis. The influence of Catholic and Orthodox churches were more pronounced in some European, South American and Asian territories. Catholics fell behind in the race to exploit and industrialise and, discovering rather late a social conscience, became vocal against science and materialism but didn't take any pro-environment role until very recently. Some of the Protestant denominations, like the Quakers and Menonites, are now taking up the pro-environment programme disowning the concept of man's domination of nature. When the scriptures of God are usurped by man and revised in the name of the new god 'Progress', these errors are bound to happen.

Human knowledge pertains to a time and circumstance but divine providence is eternal. Some scientists and ecologists, in the bedazzlement of science's technical achievements, may think differently, but their knowledge is notoriously ever changing and limited. So people of the revelation should bravely come forward with the light of divine guidance. In the book *Ecology and Christianity*, Cassell, London, pp. 98 it is stated:

> "There is much to be done, and Christianity has a large part to play in the struggle to save the earth from environmental destruction. First of all, the Church has to change itself – in praise and celebration of the Creator and Sustainer of the Earth, and in practical action. The vision will need to have a new theology – a new understanding of God, a new morality – a new understanding of human beings and their responsibilities."[66]

This is exactly what the first and final revelation to mankind – Islam – wants you to do, as will be seen below. Historian Lynn White presented a paper, *The Historic Roots of our Economic Crisis*, in 1967 before the American Association for the Advancement of Science wherein he held that the teaching of Genesis is the root cause of environmental degradation.

> "Be fertile and multiply; fill the earth and subdue it. Have domain over the fish of the sea, the birds of the

air and all living things that move on this earth." (Genesis 1: 28)

Al Gore in his *Earth in the Balance* posed a similar question: "When giving us the dominion over the Earth, did God choose an appropriate technology?" The Christian jury that thinks it can pass judgement on God is still out. Sane people who realise that it is always man who is accountable can't accept this question as formulated. Indeed, what is at issue here is human greed making use of the vagueness of a partially remembered tradition or old revelation. But an eminent 'juror' – Prince Phillip of Great Britain – made no secret of his verdict in his introduction to the book, *Save the Earth*[67]:

> "To me, that Old Testament story has provided Western man, accompanied by Judaeo-Christian heritage, with an overbearing and domineering attitude towards God's creation. By contrast, the Koran specifically mentions the fact that the natural world is loaned from God, a trust or stewardship."

The Prince calls for a 'spiritual readjustment' with 'technological ability'. The above book was a call to save the earth from environmental pollution and a call to arms by many of the world's renowned scientists, political and religious leaders, authors and artists. This was published in 1991, well before the Rio World Summit on Environment and Development.

Fortunately today all the hierarchies of the religions including Judaism and Christianity are taking positive pro-life and pro-environment roles, and trying hard to forget their past roles, as evidenced in the Assisi Declaration of 1986 by a group of people representing most of the religions. The developing role of the National Religious Partnership for the Environment of USA and the Islamic Foundation for Ecology and the Environment of UK are noteworthy. Some are still sectarian in their approach and programme but we should look forward to their realistic appreciation of the desperate urgency of the situation. Even the UNEP is now looking into the moral core of the issue of combating the degradation as we have already pointed out above.

Father Lanfranco Serrini, in the Assisi Declaration, calls for:

> "a synthesis between culture and faith; ecumenical dialogue on the goals of scientific research and on the environmental consequences of the use of its findings; the priority of moral values over technological advances; truth, justice and the peaceful coexistence of all peoples."[53]

Some may consider this a trick to try and keep a seat at a table from which they are increasingly being edged away by the vast majority of people who have seen through the fraudulence of their doctrine, and the historical evil of their actions. When they had power there was no talk of ecumenicism, because they then had the Inquisition and that was quite enough. But let us keep open the doors for the present.

4.2. Zoroastrianism, Buddhism, Hinduism and Sikhism

Zoroastrianism

Zoroastrianism is another very old religion but almost extinct except in some parts of Iran and India. The religion deteriorated into a belief in fire worship to the eternal spirit. Zoroaster, in Persian called Zarathustra, was born in Media and lived there in ancient Persia about 600 years before 'Isa, 'alaihi's-salam, at the time of King Cyrus (529 BC) and Darius 1 (558-486 BC). Originally his preaching may have been unitarian, without worship of idols, as had been the teachings of Ibrahim and Musa, 'alaihima's-salam.

Their deity was Ahura Mazda, the wise Lord. Zarathustra proclaimed faith in one God and denounced idolatry and the evil Ahriman. According to him man and the universe were created by the Lord, and man returns to the Lord Who also gave nature its laws. His book of hymns (gathas) was known as Zend Avesta and existed about 250 years before Alexander. The source of violence and fury in their thinking is Ahriman, who will be defeated by Ahura Mazda after 9,000 years according to Zarathustra. The sense of dualism is very strong, good and evil being treated as two great spiritual powers of truth and falsehood, whose struggle is for the salvation of man. There are elements of this dualistic teaching which very definitely inform the version of Christianity that has come down to us. Dualism is opposed to true tawhid that sees all good and harm as springing from Allah, exalted and glorious is He. In Zoroastrianism the good will cross the bridge and the bad ones will be dropped in the fire below at the end. The good spirit of Ahura Mazda is not a God but a spirit which is surrounded by seven powers and the bad spirit of Ahriman is surrounded by demons, according to their belief.

After the spread of Islam in Persia in the 7th century some of them migrated to India and other places, but most of them accepted Islam as a benevolent religion like their original faith. Zoroastrians are supposed to be compassionate to humans, animals and other beings as a sign of their goodness but they must not worship them. Sacrifice and eating of animals are not forbidden in their religion, but they cannot squander or waste. Those who still follow this faith are respectful towards nature and the environment. Their places of worship are known as fire temples which used initially to be without any idols, but later Mitra, Vayu, Yama and Deva were introduced by deviant followers. Zoroastrians generally are quite friendly to the environment.

Buddhism

Buddhism is one of the other old religions which still survive in Asia. Later Buddhists speculate that it may be older than Hinduism and they hold the belief in the historical Buddha as one appearance in a long line of Buddhas. The Hindus as usual added the Buddha as a new god to their pantheon. Maybe the incorporation was done after the Buddha's time by Hindu theologians trying to adapt themselves to the mighty influence of Buddhist culture in India. This religion dates back to the birth of the Buddha, 563 years before the Christian era.

Gautama was a prince but he left the palace to find out the wisdom of life and to be rid of all the sorrows and sufferings he saw around him. He spent years in austerities and yogic practices, as well as in mastering the obscurities of Hindu metaphysics. He finally abandoned all of that and meditated under a forest tree (bodha) until he became enlightened by inspiration – a Buddha – with the wisdom he was seeking. From his self-imposed exile in the forests he came back to society and taught the wisdom he had found to the people of his kingdom. He ceased to be Gautama, the prince, but became Buddha, the enlightened. However, he selected his abode in the forests instead of going back to the palace.

One of the most important teachings of Buddhism, particularly stressed by some schools more than others, is to develop loving kindness and compassion for all things and beings in order to attain human salvation.

Buddhism doesn't talk of a creator or the world hereafter, because of the Buddha's disgust with the futility of Hindu theology. It talks of salvation from suffering acknowledging the importance of 'karma' i.e. the cumulative effect of deeds. He taught the need for kindness and the wish to help others to be happy through their liberation from suffering, and he taught his followers to be compassionate and to wish to alleviate all suffering; be it through sickness, poverty or death. His teaching also was in keeping morals pure in action: not to commit evil but to practice all good and to keep the heart pure. (Dhammapada).

By extending love and care to all things and beings in nonviolence, Buddhism is supposed to become closer to fitrah and the environment. Though the Hindus took some of his lessons like nonviolence into their own faith, and later Buddhists regressed and took some parts of Hinduism – like reincarnation – they were always at daggers drawn. Buddhism was forced out of India by the Hindus and north of the Himalayas to China after the rule of Ashoka in India and south to Sri Lanka, and east to Korea, Vietnam and Japan. By accepting the Dalai Lama of Tibet in exile, India did not wish to accept Buddhism back to its original land, but she served her geopolitical interests against Peoples' China. The Dalai Lama is now sheltering in the USA with his Buddhist followers and is a great patron of environmental protection.

The object of morality in Buddhism is to create the conditions of a spiritual fulfilment which is known to them as Nirvana. In Buddhism, Karma and Nirvana are treated as both physical and mental. All actions begin in the mind so its motivation, discipline and concentration are needed for meditation, a deep form of Buddhist Yoga, which is something akin to prayer. In good deeds and in desisting from evil lie salvation. Deeds permeate the entire field of things and beings including nature. Sense orientation towards nature – its interrelated things and beings – is the sheet anchor of Buddhist teaching. Humans are interrelated and dependent on nature so must serve, not dominate, over the environment. Man must love and be full of compassion also for all beings. Buddhists believe that humans have a unique opportunity which other creatures don't have to realise enlightenment, but that superiority can only be realised while in harmony with the interconnectedness of everything. Not by domination or exploitation of nature can you be enlightened, but by being an integral part of it you may.

The only trace of original Buddhist scriptures or books are those recorded in Sri Lanka in the 1st century C.E. in the Pali language of the Magadha kingdom of India. The later narrations in Tibetan, Chinese, Japanese and other languages do not always correspond to each other but the basic theme of love and compassion remains the same in the Tripitaka (3 baskets). The several sutras (canons) of the Pali Canon (Tripitaka) speak of the close relationship between human morality and the natural environment. Human morals influence not only the psychological make-up of the people but also the biological and physical environment as well. While taking benefits of natural bounties like food, drink, clothing, shelter, air, medicine, etc., man must learn to satisfy his essential needs and not to feed his insatiable greed or his habit of waste. Buddhists are expected to take a nonviolent course not only to all living beings but also to things like vegetables, forests and hills. They use these but with care and within limits. Nowadays they also eat fish and flesh, which theoretically they can only do if offered the meat by the practitioner of another religion who is permitted to eat meat, since they are not permitted to take life. This led in Tibet to their dependence on Muslims for their meat, since in the extremely cold climate of the Himalayas there is no avoiding the necessity of animal protein in the diet.

The Buddha's whole life was associated with forests so his disposition was never to exploit or plunder them as Buddhists are doing today. A few years ago I was in Bangkok on a Saudi Arabian Airlines' business trip. With so much smoke, *tuktuk* noise and crowds seeking sex with prostitutes in the city, I felt suffocated. The last time I was there our Saudi delegation escaped to the seaside Pataya by courtesy of the Thai government. This time I booked my flight to Chang Mai in the hilly north of deep forests.

When I landed at the airport I found wide open horizons of land and bush. The limousine took me up the winding road to the hilly town. When I asked the driver how far away was the deep forest, he stared at me with annoyance and asked me: "Are you also one of those from the World Bank who are trying to throw us off our land?" I was surprised but I had to tell him that I worked for an airline, not for any bank which takes and gives interest to exploit the people. What the driver in his broken English and pacific voice explained to me, almost in tears was this:

"There was no airport, no industry and no big buildings in Chang Mai in my young days, but we had thick forests and huts on the hills and in the valley of Mai Soi. We had enough to eat, plentiful rainwater and a peaceful environment with forests and rivers. We Buddhists are peaceful people, so we had friendly relations with the minority Christians and Muslims and never had any big crisis or disaster. A few white people came from the West as tourists to see the natural beauty, and are reported to have done some trade also for our prosperity. Cars, tractors, bulldozers and other machinery came, roads were made, buildings were built and I like some others got a job. We were becoming prosperous, our business grew and our country earned foreign currency for development. Christian missionary nuns came with free education, food and medicine, slowly converting us to Christianity. Even the World Bank later came to develop Mai Soi valley."

"So what happened?" I asked.

"Away with the development and so-called prosperity went our forests, the soil eroding, making rain scarce, agricultural production diminished, farmers looking for rare jobs and social contentment evaporated. Our girls were sold to foreign tourists in the clubs and brothels of Bangkok. Away with the forests went our natural building materials, fuels, crops, forest fruits, natural drinks and herbal medicines. We had starved the goose which laid the golden eggs. The government came in to plant eucalyptus and for selective logging but their agents finally killed the starving goose. The World Bank came for a sure rescue with a project for a rain-fed reservoir system in the valley, worth millions of Bhats. But that also proved to be the last peg in the coffin as there was not as much rain to fill those huge reservoirs as estimated by the top technocrats of the World Bank towers in America."

I am narrating this story which pertains to Buddhist Thailand where love and compassion should rule in nature and society under the shadows of a thousand Buddhist Pagodas. Within the last two decades Thailand has lost nearly 80% of its natural forests. The cases of China which is partially Confucianist, Taoist and Buddhist, Japan which is Shintoist and Buddhist, and, Korea, Vietnam and Burma, which are predominantly Buddhist, are not very different. The craze for development has set up industries, mechanised cultivation with fertilisers, uprooted rural tribes, concentrated labour in shanty towns and polluted air, water and land throughout modern Thailand.

This deforestation and subsequent degradation of the environment equally applies in densely populated Muslim Indonesia and Malaysia, Christian Europe and America and Hindu India and Nepal. Nowadays we all are victims of material greed and apathy towards religion in the name of secularism or socialism. The way out is to change our attitude towards the religion called 'development and progress' intellectually and practically, whether we are Buddhists or not so that we can save humanity and the environment from a total collapse unitedly. The reality is that the technological religion has supplanted all religions to such an extent that they are now irrecoverable, so that people of good will have now no real choice but to embrace Islam which alone has what is needed to face this challenge.

The Venerable Lungrig Namgyal Rinpoche records in the Assisi Declaration:

> "Side by side with the exploration of outer space, there is the continuing pollution of the lakes, rivers and vast

parts of the oceans, out of human ignorance and misunderstanding. There is a great danger that future generations will not know the natural habitat of animals; they may not know the forests and the animals which we of this generation know to be in danger of extinction. We are the generation with the awareness of a great danger. We are the ones with the responsibility and the ability to take steps of concrete action, before it is too late."[53]

The sad truth is that many people are saying exactly the same thing, and it amounts to nothing, and it may already be too late. For example, some environmentalists have said that even if we were to shut down the entire technological project today, it would not immediately stop global warming, and indeed not for some time. We are in a predicament which we have thought our way into and from which we may not think our way out, and which is impossible of resolution except by a heartfelt turning to Allah as abject slaves who regret the sorry mess we have made of the earth, and who earnestly seek His guidance in the affair.

Hinduism

Hinduism is one of the oldest religions on the earth as historians date it back 5,000 years. To that degree it is also the way of people who have consistently rejected the more recent revelations and Messengers of the Divine. The most insidious form of rejection of a Messenger is to ignore his teachings and worship him as a deity, as the Christians well know. This is the path the Hindus have long since adopted. If we turn to the ancient books and one studies this religion one finds in essence that it believes in a supreme Creator and His creation of the earth with all things and beings. They call that creator Vishnu, Bhagabhan or Brahma. But the creed itself has taken all the powers of their Creator and divided them among forms and idols of mud, stone, wood, metal, paintings and millions of images. They worship their millions of gods and goddesses in their homes, temples and different holy sites all over India and beyond, while maintaining their distinct caste divisions.

Amongst the many sects and branches of Hinduism, Baishnabism and Shivaism are the main and their common source is the books of Veda, Gita and Mahabharat. The name Hindu is not from their religious sources at all, rather it was derived from the river Indus which flowed from the Himalayan Hindu Kush to the Indian Ocean through the north-western part of the subcontinent, now entirely in Pakistan. Like Judaism its name is related to a place and not to its faith. Their followers are known accordingly – as Hindus or Jews – though many of them now live outside India or Judaea. Geography changes in time, humans modify the revelation and the teaching but the true way of Allah, as finally completed in the revelation to Sayyiduna Muhammad, salla'llahu 'alaihi wa sallam, will last as long as the world does, without geographical boundaries or human corruption.

Rivers and forests, these important parts of the environment, are the cradles of the Hindu religion. The river Ganges, whose water they drink and where they bathe, is treated as one of their gods and known as Mother Ganga, and the forests of Brindaban near Delhi are also like a deity to them, where their god Krishna and goddess Radha used to reside and play on the bank of another river named Jamuna. The waters of these two and many other rivers of India today are practically unfit for drinking or bathing in due to heavy pollution. Deforestation and urbanisation have also ruined the forests of Brindaban like other forests of India creating a serious ecological crisis there.

Numerically Hinduism occupies the fourth place after Christianity, Islam and Buddhism, but by historical tradition and religious plurality India is regarded as a major country of material consequence. So the UN, the World Bank, superpowers and neighbours give them due weight, but ecologically India is in such a mess and no-one but their own people can save it from the disaster. The Indian people are mostly Hindus by faith although there is a surprisingly large and growing population of Muslims who live in some danger to their lives from fanatical Hindus. A great responsibility lies on Hindus' shoulders, and instead of relying on fanatical conflicts with others over theological and sectarian issues that have little reality in the age in which we live, they should turn towards addressing the issues of real consequence, one of which is the destruction of the environment, which if they seriously paid attention to they would find was merely the tip of a huge iceberg threatening humanity as a whole. Ultimately, the destruction that is most to be feared is not only a painful and frightening death in a destroyed and polluted planet, but it is the anguish of returning to one's Lord and having to render account for a life wasted in the worship of the false gods of this strange era we live in, and of having to live with that anguish through all eternity.

India is not one of the pioneers of industrial revolution so it is in a relatively safe zone with abundant resources of water, forest, manpower and minerals. Instead of destroying its forests, diverting or polluting its abundant river waters and seas, building its chemical and nuclear plants for creating weapons of destruction and superpower warmongering against its neighbours under the umbrella of non-alignment, Indian Hinduism could build up their religious values of nonviolence and the interconnectedness of all things in nature to save the degradation of the environment. They could do that, if there were any living transmission left within Hinduism, but as we said, the Buddha sought for that in vain more than two millennia ago.

The incarnation is a popular theme in the Hindu Vedas. As Muslims we could interpret the doctrine if we were being charitable that it is an expression of the understanding that contemplation of the creation reveals different names and attributes of the Creator. Incarnation is exemplified in ten lives, one after the other: 1. Fish – Matsya, 2. Turtle – Kurma, 3. Boar – Baraha, 4. Male-Lion – Narashimha, 5. Dwarf – Bamana, 6. Warrior – Parshurama, 7. King – Rama, 8. Cowherd – Balarama, 9. Teacher – Buddha, 10. Slayer – Kali.

These forms of life, however mythological and whatever interpretation we put on them, denote a close link with the creation, especially the fish, turtle, boar, lion and cowherd. In all types of worship, whether they offer it to their goddess Kali (fury), Saraswati (learning), Durga (luck), Ganesh (wealth), Rama (king), Krishna (cowboy) or when they physically offer fruits, flowers, leaves, food and water to them before they eat as 'prashad', though they sacrifice animals before their gods and goddesses in their festivals with music and dance they are supposed to indicate devotion and respect to nature by their faith.

The Indian government professes the virtues in some mythological stories which could very well help educated Hindus to restore their confidence in the value of the forests and waters along with the need to keep the atmosphere clean (*pabitra*) from pollution. Some of their activists are putting their efforts to save the country from deforestation, water pollution, urbanisation and industrial pollution, but high caste Hindus are busy struggling, involved in their religious fanaticism or money making.

The Indian government today, with the help of the UN, other environmental agencies and ecologists themselves, have many projects for the management and control of environmental problems. It is the responsibility of the Government no doubt but the primary responsibility is with the people who have to be aware of and motivated by the cause of the environment, i.e. the ordinary people and businessmen. It could be said that this can best be done in India by the religious consciousness of its Hindu, Muslim, Buddhist and Christian populations through coordination, not hostility. However, as we have said, it is only Islam that connects by transmission to a genuine living current of teaching and knowledge. It is similarly only the Muslims that have not been entirely swept away by the religion of the age, 'production and consumption', and indeed often where they have been severely eroded they have often displayed the potential for growing back after almost seemingly impossible odds against doing so. The population of India by tradition and practice were accustomed to simple living and high thinking in the early days of Hindu and Buddhist rule and that was preserved for them through the seven centuries of Muslim rule in spite of their failing in the majority to embrace Islam.

The Western occupation of almost two centuries and the post-independence period of about fifty years have made these people easy targets for the beasts of prey called capitalism and communism which are out for material benefits rather than enlightenment or salvation. They talk of Hinduism, socialism and democracy in the same breath but are boastful of their material prosperity and the military development of the Government but far less proud of the condition of their people.

Their stance of secularism in essence is guided by their western-educated high caste, and even low caste elites who do not like the discriminatory caste system and Hindu fanaticism. Hindu polytheism and the caste system divide their followers into four distinct classes: Brahmins who are the high priestly class, Khatrias the warrior class, Sudras the working class, and Harijans the scheduled lowest class. They do not intermix socially and cannot eat, drink or even worship together. To worship any of the gods, Brahmin priests have to conduct the services in temples. The two lower castes are not even allowed to hear, read or touch their holy book the Veda or marry into higher castes. Even Dr. Radhakrishnan in his book, *Eastern Religions and Western Thoughts*, tried to justify this inhuman caste system.[68] International Human Rights organisations do not take up the cause of these downtrodden and persecuted millions of low caste Hindus of India, although they are vociferous in many less pressing areas.

The two lower castes do all the manual work, like farming, fishing, forestry and manufacturing. So the lower castes are actually engaged in cultivating, nourishing and protecting nature around India, whereas the high castes either enjoy or damage it at will. The Brahmin overlordship in religion has also extended to the landlordship of lands, agriculture, forests, fisheries and water and far beyond into the modern world of finance and administration. The biggest world democracy with a per capita income of about $200 per annum and about 20% percent of the population receiving any education has wrought some visible material changes in the country but their socio-religious structure still remains deeply rooted in the caste system to the serious detriment of both humanity and the environment.

The legend of Ramayan depicts Ram as a war hero who defeats the Sri Lankan king Ravan to free his wife Sita. But his life in exile was in the forests of Ayodha and the companions in his fight against Ravan were monkeys (*hanuman*) of the forests which shows the nearness to nature of the tradition and the closeness to animals. Their other god Krishna not only had his habitat in the forests of Brindaban on the banks of river Jamuna but he also worshipped the nearby Gobardhan hill and sun god.

Their Jain sect advocates nonviolence (*ahimsa*) as the greatest good and that on no account should life be taken. Gandhi followed their dictum and many Hindus still do. Their migration to the cities today is not only fashionable but necessitated by their politico-economic order of domination by the high castes. In the cities the low castes are not strictly bound by caste distinctions. The privileged high caste Hindus still dominate the cities in the marathon for higher education, better jobs, more cars, superior housing, more jewellery, bigger bank balances and industrial prosperity. In the rural areas the lower castes have no opportunity to compete with the high castes but massive urbanisation has opened that door ajar.

In the post-independence period (since 1947) India has no doubt become industrially and militarily strong, but at a great cost to the traditional social, moral and spiritual values of its people. The ultimate victims are its common people who suffer abject poverty, illiteracy, poor health, bad hygiene, depleted foods and a lack of shelter. Over 800 million people (about 75% of whom are Hindus and 80% illiterate) now suffer acute environmental pollution of the air, land and water hitherto unnoticed by the authorities.

India is rich in natural resources of coal and oil but more than 50% of them are being wasted on military spending. By building high dams, like the one proposed in Tehri across the Bhagirath-Ganges rivers, and the one already built at Farrakah with deforestation and industrial pollution, India is displacing its population and highly polluting its natural environment. By burning fossil fuels, by huge deforestation, industrial and municipal discharges and by fumes from vehicles throughout India from the Himalayas to the Indian ocean, environmental degradation has gone too far.

It is time for her and other developing countries to realise that natural resources are not only for waste and trade but they are an integral part of their lives and their survival. The WWF's report of 1990 in *Community Bio-Diversity* says:

> "Time is running out. Unless we take immediate steps to make every child, woman and man of India a partner as well as a beneficiary of the conservation movement, we will be silent spectators of one of the greatest biological tragedies in human history."[69]

This conservation is possible only with the social, moral and ethical commitment of the enlightened people of India, and it is only possible with the guidance of the Lord of Creation which is only expressed in this age by the way of Islam. If we believed that technological and scientific solutions to the environmental problem could be found and would be sufficient, we would be subscribing to the very thesis which is the source of the plague that has devastated the planet. However, we are not calling for an anti-intellectual religiosity since we are all too well aware of the nature of that beast. Rather revelation is the light of the intellect without which man cannot see, let alone think. Similarly, if we were to make the environmental problem the focus of all people irrespective of religion we would by that make it the religion. Our position as Muslims is that the perilous state of the environment is just one more indication of our remoteness from our Lord and our disobedience of His Messenger, salla'llahu 'alaihi wa sallam. If we only turned to the environment we would be like the doctor who treating only the symptoms of the patient neglects the underlying cause and so prescribes a remedy which covers over the symptom for a while until it erupts elsewhere in a more malign form.

Dr. Karan Singh writes in Assisi Declaration:

> "Let us declare our determination to halt the present slide towards destruction, to rediscover the ancient tradition of reverence for all life and, even at this late hour to reverse the suicidal course upon which we have embarked. Let us recall the ancient Hindu dictum: 'The earth is our mother, and we are all her children'."[53]

This poetically sounds attractive, but it has inherent in it the possibility of idolisation of the earth which is not only prohibited to us, but would be entirely unhelpful at this point in our situation. Rather, as the Muslims understand let us say rather that Allah is our Lord, and we are all His creatures and slaves. We are honoured to be His custodians of the earth and of all life, and entrusted with the terrible responsibility of being answerable for our actions and for our inactions.

Sikhism

In 1649 a child was born in the village of Tavandi in Punjab, India, in the family of one Kalu. His parents named him with affection, Nanak. When the child grew up, the caste system and idol worship of his Hindu religion worried him a great deal. His liberal thinking made him a reformer to remove all the pride and prejudices of the then Hindu society while accepting the benevolent ingredients of both Hindu and Islamic religions. Indeed, he is reputed to have received instruction from some Muslims. Thus Nanak the child became Guru Nanak [1539-1649] the teacher to his followers.

He gathered a good number of followers around him. His sayings and hymns with those of his nine successor Gurus were recorded in the Punjabi language of Gurumuki known as Guru Granth Sahib. So the Gurus and their teachings became the religion of Sikhism. Now strongly prevalent in East Punjab and spread out in other parts of India and other countries of the world the Sikhs play an important role in history. They are not very big in number but very conspicuous in their dress code of the five Kakkars i.e. kesh (uncut hair), kangha (comb), Kara (iron bangle), kirpan (sword) and kacca (short pants). The turban is not a part of kakkars, but must be worn by all khalsa Sikhs. The last of the ten Gurus, Govind Singh [1666-1708], introduced the fighting khalsa group and the compulsory dress code in 1699.

Sikhs pray at home and in congregation in Gurdwarwas with a copy of Granth Sahib, men and women sitting separately. They believe in One God Who may not be likened to any created thing and in a casteless society like the Muslims, but celebrate their festivals with dance and music like the Hindus. Like other religions they also developed many sects (Khalsa, Nirankari, Namdhari, etc.). When Sikhism repeatedly rubbed shoulders with Islam, Hinduism and Christianity in India, Europe and America, Sikhs changed many of their religious practices to liberal ones.

However, we must note here that Sikhism is not a genuine religion in the sense of any of the others we have considered. Muslims have always given the benefit of the doubt to Zoroastrians, Buddhists and even Hindus that they are Peoples of the Book, since Allah, exalted and glorious is He, has told us that He has sent prophets to every people in every epoch. However, we know for certain that there is no prophet after the Last Messenger and Prophet, salla'llahu 'alaihi wa sallam, and so we have no doubt that Guru Nanak was not a prophet with a revelation from the Divine and a commission to found a community. Perhaps we can only understand him as a Hindu who came close to Islam, but in the end opted for founding a sect of Hinduism, which nevertheless was hostile to Hinduism itself.

From an environmental point of view there are some sayings in Guru Granth Sahib. Cleansing with water is obligatory on all Sikh men and women before performing prayers. Kind treatment of plants, animals, birds and fish are strongly recommended. When talking of pollution they understand pollution of morality more than of the environment, which no doubt is very laudable. But environmental awareness is very essential for all the Sikhs as is their political goal of Khalistan.

4.3. The Science and Technology of Communism and Capitalism

Marxian Communism is not, by its own criteria, a religion but a dogma of material prosperity. However, it is clear that in replacing religion it became itself one in the lives of its adherents. This religion enchanted and motivated a few idealists of the West to try and get rid of the socio-economic exploitation of autocratic rulers and centuries-long Church domination. Even Plato in his *Republic* talked of a type of communism in the pre-Christian era, but it is Marx and Engels of the 19th century who crystalised the gospel of communism into the vision of a classless society which would be brought about by the fight of the working class against capitalism.

"The history of hitherto existing society is the history of class struggle", was the opening declaration of *Das Kapital*, the bible of Marxism. It initiated a "class war" to be waged by the have-nots against rich capitalists until the whole world is conquered by them. "Each according to his need and each according to his ability" was set as the norm of production and distribution of wealth, a process wherein state shall wither away. Money was a source of exploitation and so was interest so there would be no money or interest in a communist society, which however was only to be established after the interim period of the dictatorship of the proletariat. This vision, of course, ushered in a very different dictatorship than that envisioned by Marx, and it had very little idea of relinquishing its grip in favour of an egalitarian communist society.

Religion they said was the "opium of the people" so they would eliminate religion, and they actually destroyed or closed down all churches, mosques and synagogues after the Bolshevik revolution of 1917 in Russia. In that year they physically eliminated the Czar of Russia and his entire family in a most brutal massacre and established the first communist state of history, or rather the first proletarian dictatorship, except that people like Lenin and Marx had never done a day's physical work in their lives and didn't qualify to be proletarian. Under first Lenin's and then Stalin's dictatorships they ran the country into the ground, so that the ones who did not die in the prisons and the Gulags began to die of famine and starvation. This was in spite of the fact that from the very first moment of Lenin's seizure of power they were directly negotiating loans from the very capitalist banks of whom they were supposedly mortal enemies. Nevertheless, the false injections of capital could not have held the nation together. That was achieved by Hitler who in his foolhardy attempt to defeat and occupy Russia managed to unite the Russians behind Stalin, a man whom they hated. After the war they were repeatedly bailed out by aid packages from a West which was supposedly at war with them, even if only a 'cold' war. By a secret set of agreements with the Allied Powers they occupied a great deal of eastern Europe after the Second World War, including East Germany, Yugoslavia, Poland, Hungary, Czechoslovakia and their neighbouring countries. Communism quite independently subverted the ancient Chinese civilisation. Nations like Yugoslavia came out of the grip of the Russian octopus slowly, remaining communists but with a degree of autonomy, but others remained there until the collapse of the Soviet Union in Moscow in 1988, not through military conquest, revolution or *coup d'état*, but quite simply because the empire had been bankrupted by the huge debts it had to Western banks from the very first day of the revolution. Finally, the interest payments which the Politburo had been so good at keeping up (banks like dictatorships, especially military ones because they are prompt in paying their interest and don't care how hard they squeeze the people to make them pay) drained the coffers dry, the gold reserves were almost totally gone, and the ex-Soviet Union has descended into the bankrupt gangster-run Russian Federation we know today.

In the meantime communism had also engulfed Cuba, Angola, Ethiopia, North Korea, Vietnam, Burma, Indonesia and some countries of the Middle East. Only by the grace of Allah and by some adherence to the teaching of

Islam, however so slight, some countries like Egypt, Iraq and Syria in the Middle East, and Indonesia and Malaysia of South East Asia escaped communist domination even if they fell quite strongly under Soviet influence. But some Afro-Asian and European countries are still under the spell of Dracula-like communism, like a decadent paganism. It is another classic example of history that human guidance, as opposed to Divine guidance, however strong or attractive it may seem at times is nothing but the fleeting spell of an enchanting mirage.

So the downfall of the most powerful Soviet Union came about within seventy years of rising to the pinnacle of communist glory. Her superpower armed forces accepted a defeat at the hands of the small Islamic Mujahidin forces of Afghanistan; the so-called free world, in the form first of the CIA, and later the White House, supporting their fight from 1979-1990. However, as we indicated above it was the Mujahidun who defeated the Soviet Union. She had interest bearing debts. That debt had been greatly inflated by Ronald Reagan's huge 'defence' spending, a part of which was the massive 'Star Wars' programme, which forced the Soviets to try and match it dollar for dollar, thus hastening their bankruptcy. Thus we see again that the motors of history are not what people see them to be, or are shown them to be in their daily papers. We see again too the debt-finance mechanism at work here as it is in the destruction of our environment.

Capitalism is also not a religion but another human concept of material prosperity. Both communism and capitalism deny or ignore divine guidance preferring a state of worldly material superiority; the one is consciously Godless and the other is merely secular; in other words they are identical, but capitalism is if anything more dangerous because more insidious. In essence they both believe that the end justifies the means. Capitalism extols private ownership and the free market on the economic front, while repeating the slogan of secularism and freedom on the political front. Communism believes in public ownership and bonded controlled markets on the economic front with atheism and dictatorship of the proletariat (i.e. the party) on the political front. They both believe that science and technology can solve all problems. Their fertile brains are equally blank on the social, moral and spiritual phenomena of existence. So plundering the environment for their development and growth, seen in terms of GDP or GNP, was no sin or crime to them, until they reached the brink of material collapse in the field of environment.

> **"Allah has set a seal on their hearts and on their hearing. And on their eyes is a veil; for them there is a great chastisement."**
> (Qur'an 2: 7)

We will here discuss in brief the role of communism in the environment. In the book *The Greening of a Red*, Pluto Press, London, the author Malcolm MacEwen discusses the role of the communism of the USSR at some length.[90] According to him the communist party of the USSR set out, not to work with nature or its Creator, but to conquer it and recognised no limits to what man can do to control it. They tried to harness natural resources ad infinitum and produced disasters in Aral Sea water, crude industrialisation in Magnitogorsk and Nova Huta in Poland and a nuclear disaster in Chernobyl in Georgia.

Charles E . Zeigler in his book *Environmental Policy in USSR*, opines similarly:

> "Russian Marxism fell solidly in the westernising technocratic tradition. George Plenkov and his successor rejected peasant populism and romanticism in favour of 'scientific socialism'.[71] The Marxist materialistic concept embodied the 'historical determinist percep-

tion of economic growth as inherently progressive'. In their view technological development was the primary causal agent of social and political development. An agrarian society in which nature was not radically remoulded to suit civilisation's needs was by definition inferior to an industrial society. Karl Marx spoke of the 'idiocy of rural life'. Furthermore, less industrialised societies were inferior to more highly industrialised societies. Economic growth and material prosperity were by definition good."[72]

That all resources are scarce and limited doesn't fit into the Marxist framework on the environment. The value of the natural environment was totally ignored in what is after all a rather antiquated 19th century gospel of salvation for humanity. So the environment was never considered in its campaign for transforming Russia into a modern industrial society like the capitalist West. Industrial pollution went unabated in Russia and its satellite states. The Soviet Union was only second to the USA in total sulphur-dioxide emissions, with high contributions coming from Poland, East Germany, Romania, Czechoslovakia and Hungary. The official image of the environment remained fairly negative both in the Stalinist and post-Stalinist era. Besides the vastly inflated theoretical punch of Marxism, the vast size of the Soviet Union (a sixth of the earth's surface with eleven time zones) and its industrial, agricultural and natural resources made it one of the biggest world powers, with sadly no care for the environment.

The world became divided into the two superpowers of communism and capitalism and both desired to be materially superior to the other. However, rather upsettingly to this dialectical view, the capitalist world was funding the communist world all the time proving another example and proof of the saying of the Prophet, salla'llahu 'alaihi wa sallam, "Kufr is one system". After seventy of tyrannical rule the Pharaoh of communism has fallen and now the Goliath of capitalism is waiting for his material doom. Marxism held the notion that natural resources, if not inexhaustible, were at least sufficient to last into the foreseeable future. But declining oil and gold reserves, the falling clean water supply in the Aral Sea and Lake Baikal and frequent industrial and natural disasters had caused a re-examination of their prophecies in later years, specially by their environmental experts.

For the first time, in 1975-1980, environmental protection became a theme in five-year planning if only in a symbolic way. That man can neither master nor control the natural environment was beyond their revolutionary technological concept, rather it was viewed as a false plea of the reactionaries! They travelled in space, reached the moon and even fixed a space-station, MIR. Their atomic power, submarine fleet and armed forces were second to none. While denying the existence of divine law, Marxism considered even temporal laws as a part of the superstructure of pre-communist societies re-enforcing the existing inequitable social orders. But with the establishment and expansion of the Soviet state and the development of the socialist legal system, the conflict of theory and practice became more apparent. Rather, under Stalin, the socialist legal system became more sacrosanct than any divine law and its right was assumed to establish unquestionable authority for the communist party and the KGB. The latter even surpassed the notoriety of the undercover CIA with the sanction of Soviet law.

Only after Stalin's death in 1953, did reform in both civil and criminal law start to raise its unwanted face, except in political cases of liquidation or slavery. Laws to regulate the use of land, forest and water were of little significance until the last days of the 'perestroika' and 'glassnost' of Mikhail Gorbachev. Technological advance was taken by them as good and irrevocable, so industrial and atomic pollution was not considered as important as the material progress that they were making for the proletarian cause. The massive pollution caused by atomic and chemical experiments and accidents was not even made public until very recently under the pressure of environmental activists in and out of the Soviet Union. The Greenpeace movement, initiated mainly by the socialists of Western Europe, made a sizeable contribution in ecological awareness both inside and outside of Iron Curtain countries.

One can see that both communism and capitalism competed for a material prosperity in terms of a physical growth measured by GNP and GDP. They even dominated and exploited, and still do, the natural resources of the poor undeveloped countries in the name either of 'biblical dominion' or 'dictatorship of the proletariat'. The ideologies are apparently different but the actions are identical. "Kufr is one way system." They never considered moral and spiritual values as dominant factors, but then they never really wanted peaceful coexistence. They even forgot the reality that the part of a circle can never be equal to the full circle.

Man does not live by bread alone; he has a heart and a soul. Man is not the only creature in the world, even according to Darwin or Marx. How can one ignore the interrelationship of one creature with the other, the interrelationship between the sun and the moon or between the earth and other planets, the ultimate relationship of all these with the full circle of the universe under a faultless and cosmic law and order. The net result of this gigantic material pursuit without moral and spiritual guidance is the environmental catastrophe created by arrogant 'progressive' man, to his own detriment. They all have to come into the fold of the need for moral dictates of peace and order, in spite of their vocal or secret antagonism.

The fall of communism was inevitable, like all other despotic faithless regimes of history. But one should not take it as a dead horse yet. The horse still survives in other parts of the world, though not with such hateful ferocity, so it may yet be flogged to jump in any inclement weather. It is not surprising that the 'free' world of capitalism and the bonded world of communism, both having a materialistic base in their decadent stage, are now targeting the forces of peace and harmony for their own mastery. They both want to survive on agro-industrial growth, superiority with pollution, market control with interest and profiteering, advanced technology and arms supply, value-free moral degradation, media and military control.

They want the East also to join their bandwagon and share the cost of the restoration of the environment forgetting their past imperial exploitation, their plundering of natural resources and their industrial slavery. They may display beautiful things, produce splendid data or talk using nice metaphors of development, but what is in their hearts is nothing but the egocentric and amoral lust for material prosperity.

Only spiritual people with moral, peaceful and cosmological commitments can take up this challenge unitedly, sinking their man-made differences. Those people are the Muslims when they wake up to the truth of their deen, and the large numbers of the Peoples of the Book who are beginning too to wake up to the nightmare that their elites have made of the planet. When they are fully aware, they will have little choice but to enter the Ummah of Islam, the guidance of the Lord of Being to the Last Prophet for all mankind, in which alone they may unitedly 'command the good and forbid the wrong'.

4.4. Ethical and Theological Unity

Now that we have discussed and analysed briefly the various types of pollution with their effects, and also analysed the role of all the world religions and of the politico-economic domination of capitalism and communism, we can draw certain conclusions therefrom. One thing is most clear from the above, that out of all the faiths, Islam claims well laid principles of law and practice as to the different aspects affecting the environment. Be it for seawater or rain, be it for the land or its products, be it for food or drink, be it for the animals, birds or other species, be it for wind or air, be it for cleanliness or hygiene, be it for the sun or moon and for the forests, greeneries and minerals, Islamic law (Shari'ah) is well laid for their use, conservation and development.

Both the Qur'an and the Traditions speak volumes on maintaining the just balance set in the creation and the interconnection of all its creatures, which is a part of the trusteeship (Khilafah and Amanah) of mankind which the Creator has imposed on us and honoured us with. We will discuss this a little more in the chapter on the Ecological Message of Islam. For the one who is not yet clear on the basis of this research, he or she may consult that law, at least what is expressed in the Qur'an in the translations that are available and the burgeoning volume of classical works on Islamic law translated from the Arabic steadily emerging on to the book market, and find out that the divine law is the wisest and safest. That law is the fulfilment of the divine norms as laid in all the divine Books of the other Prophets, distorted fragments of which only remain to us.

Allah ta'ala demands of the followers of other religions that they accept Islam. If they do not, they should live under the just governance of Islam and pay the jizyah. Allah ta'ala generously allows the People of the Book to live by their own revelations under the governance of Islam. No other revelation has any provision for interacting with the remnants of previous revelations. It is a proof of the finality of the revelation of Islam and of its character as a global deen for all mankind. Within that safe and protected zone, the People of the Book may have some creditable contributions in this field of the environment, so they should not be ignored, rather their followers in this field should be encouraged. However, we are not yet in that safe zone. The hostile media publicity, animosity, antagonism and violence against each other of the religions are inevitable in the unrestrained conditions of a planet without shari'ah or the guiding hand of a Khalifah, where the Peoples of the Book act without any limits imposed on them.

The Lord is not happy with the aggressor, rather in peace and love is His glory. That is why He guided mankind to the way that leads to peace from the early days of Adam and Ibrahim, 'alaihima's-salam. In the law and the order of the universe, this peace and love with just balance is eloquently inherent in everything that abides in air, water and land. We all have to appreciate and preserve that order in the name of Allah and not damage or destroy it in the names of science, technology, rationalism, market forces, democracy and a thousand other demonstrable idols.

All people of Iman must act together on this vital issue. Judaism, Christianity, Hinduism and Buddhism have not within themselves that which can win this battle to save the environment, for indeed they are the ones battling to destroy the environment, except for the gallant few. They fought many battles against Islam, and it is this battle of which the environment is now the sore loser. Ultimately, the entrenched Judaeo-Christian West was ever on the defence against a continuously renewed and resurgent Islam from the time of the first community up until the time of the Ottomans who twice took the jihad to gates of Vienna.

In its resolute determination not to accept the Messenger of Allah, salla'llahu 'alaihi wa sallam, it came up with the twins, science and technology, which when driven by the merciless engine of usury finance have caused so much sorrow. Newton's mechanics was so elegant in its science, and in its calculation of celestial orbits. In other hands it is nothing other than the calculation of trajectile paths, the basis of all artillery, and its logical outcome was the slaughter of the First World War where the big guns on both sides pounded the humans in the trenches to pieces. Similarly, it is the calculation of forces and stresses which are ultimately expressed in the motions of the machinery that drove the industrial revolution. The very science which overthrew Newton, Quantum Mechanics, has a quite abstract and mathematical nature which has thrown up an intriguing metaphysical speculation. In the wrong hands it merely gifted the world with the atomic bomb, which might yet cause great havoc on the earth, if the monstrous terror of the Cold War was not human havoc enough. To see into the essential causes of the pollution, and to renounce the culture that could cause it are enough. To see into the essential nature of the culture of Islam, which is surrender to cosmic order of which the shari'ah is just an expression in the human domain, and then to stand firm in creating a sane society on that base is worth more than the fight against a symptom such as pollution.

The acceptance finally by the People of the Book of the truth of the Messenger of Allah, salla'llahu 'alaihi wa sallam, is the only thing which will bring all of mankind closer to unity, peace and prosperity. The foundation of this unity cannot be laid by pious words alone like the Assisi Declaration.

As to capitalism and communism we are really flabbergasted by their ungodly acts. One poses to be the saviour of mankind by a ruthless dictatorship, in the name of the proletariat, suppressing all religions and devastating natural resources, preventing the human's obligation to worship and the right to equitable and just treatment. The other in the name of progress, during and after the industrial revolution, sucked the blood of the less privileged (by domination and exploitation), polluting the global environment under the banner of civilisation, liberty, democracy and the free market economy. Both these vampires are waiting to be nailed in the chest before they drain the life-blood of the green earth and its people.

Environmental ethics are not a muddle, rather they are an invitation to moral and social development. They are ecocentric for non-Muslims but must be theocentric (God-centred) for Muslims and in contradistinction to materialistic egoism. Ecological conscience, for Muslims, springs from a genuine respect for all things and beings in virtue of their self-evident proclamation of the presence of their Originator. This inspiration should guide our conduct in conservation and in balanced development as opposed to amoral and immoral destruction and exploitation, which are the converse of the above, crude and barbaric treatment of the creatures and the creation in denial of their Creator. It is not that we crave for high material superiority, rather only a higher social existence should be our goal, for a better life of balance, order and peace. For this we have to understand our ethical responsibility to ourselves and to all the other interrelated things and beings.

But as far as misguided man is concerned he has drawn the conclusion of his own imminent end by himself creating the catastrophe. Yet the future is unknown and unknowable to all except to our Lord Originator. So we have to rely on His mercy and try to find the best human solution to meet the catastrophe. With that intention and objective in mind we have to develop a common strategy to fight the burning fire for the sake of humanity.

In the light of the above let us accept the following three principles irrespective of our nation, colour, language, or our religious, political or economic differences as we have seen that mankind is potentially one, the earth is one and the supreme law of the universe is one:

1. That our earth and the universe and all things and beings in it are creations of One Power who in His infinite wisdom has set all in a well-measured balance for their existence.

2. And the man of the planet earth being His finest creation is a creature interdependent with the rest of creation, but gifted with certain obligations and trusts (*amanat*) to his Lord, and to himself and to all others as a representative and trustee of his Lord The creation, the creatures, its benefits and its balance must not be violated by any trustee or his institutions to the detriment of others. We all must educate ourselves in this ethical responsibility and preserve it at all costs. There is no possibility of global action, which the impending environmental catastrophe demands, unless there is a common understanding. It is unthinkable that this should be on the merely secular and utilitarian base of modern scientific and sceptical agnosticism.

The followers of all religions especially the Muslims must stop looking at themselves as if they were football club supporters, and must see themselves as worshippers of Allah who follow prophets. Through their global organisations like OIC, WML, IIRO, Islamic Centres and others the Muslim could form a unified environmental organisation to develop a common strategy of action in collaboration with others. Muslims must educate themselves on the latest facts and data of the environment and equip themselves with moral and technological know-how and practise it themselves as good examples to others. The enlightened Muslims (including the *'ulama*) ought to be fully aware of the problem, and give up their minor differences for the noble effort of jihad in the cause of Allah. It is clear that the once noble project of western civilisation has been hijacked by forces which will only be countered with a struggle. All the Muslim Governments (55 today) must join together in seeking to implement the shari'ah, not merely as a sacred relic of the past but as the only force that can possibly save humanity, since it is only Allah Who can save us now, and we need not expect His help without our obedience to Him.

If we still believed that world governmental organisations were something other than expressions of various vested interests seeking to guard their investments, we would call for the UN, all states, local and global NGOs on the environment, and welfare, research and health centres to recast their policies to incorporate theological, humane and ethical values in their environmental programme and enforce them through local, national and international laws with public awareness and collaboration. However, despite our knowledge of the good will of many who are in these organisations, we have no faith in their ability to achieve anything, since the 'dog does not bite the hand that feeds it'.

The countries most responsible for this catastrophe (industrialised West and East) would logically have to accept the greater burden of correction to save themselves and others, but we do not live in a logical world. The policies of 'dominion', 'domination', 'mastery', 'leadership' over nature, resources, men and other beings, and the dream of some 'utopia' in the future must be obliterated to beat the disaster. A programme to reduce overall pollution needs to be charted out for implementation in all sectors of air, land and water both on local and global bases, but the clear truth is that the mad age of usurious finance must be stopped. We are not against industry and science, but driven by modern banking and financial methods they are the very death of humanity.

The Prophet Muhammad, salla'llahu 'alaihi wa sallam, said:

> "Whoever of you sees a wrong, he should change it with his hand; and if he cannot do that (he should change it) with his tongue; and if he cannot do that, (he should change it) with his heart and that is the weakest of faith."
> (Sahih Muslim)[26]

According to ecologists, the world temperature remained fairly constant for 10,000 years until the industrial revolution came. Today it is a few degrees higher and at the present rate it will rise some more. That doesn't sound very serious, but it must be remembered that the average increase in temperature since the middle of the last ice age has been five degrees Celsius. That is the difference between middle England under a sheet of ice and middle England harvesting wheat. Since the end of the last ice age, 10,000 years ago, average temperatures have increased by only 2°C. At the current rate of warming we will experience exactly the same increase in less than a century. Britain and some other countries have reported warmer climates since 1980. In the beginning, the scientists of Russia and of the USA dismissed the greenhouse effect as "the laugh of the century". But the repeated tsanumis, tornadoes, cyclones and floods in Japan, Brazil, Mexico, Jamaica and Bangladesh (1970, 1988 and 1990) and even in the USA, Germany, France, Spain and Italy (1990-96) have cost millions of human, animal and other lives and billions of dollars worth of material assets in recent times. Just watch and ponder over one week's global disasters and tell us how we can laugh. Statistical data for November 1st-7th of 1994 alone, showed the following disasters: rainstorms with floods in France, China, Spain and Italy, thunderstorms with high winds in Australia, Egypt and Israel and cyclones with floods in India.

Scientists now estimate that the amount of CO_2 in the atmosphere was originally 270 parts per million, which had risen 30% by 1988 and may have increased 100% by the 21st Christian century. The US Environmental Protection Agency, the Institute of Applied Systems Analysis of Austria and similar agencies now assess that there will have been a rise of 1.5 to 5 degrees Celsius in temperature both to the north and south of the equator soon. Nowadays the opinion is almost unanimous that the greenhouse effect will cause a rise in seawater levels by heating oceans, and glaciers and ice caps in the Arctic and Antarctic inundating the low-lying areas of the world. So the greenhouse effect in the atmosphere above has already attacked the ground and water below and man is trapped in between by his own deeds in this disaster. The remedy is practical action with social commitment.[73]

4.5. The Ecological Message of Islam

Islam is the way of tawhid as were the ways of the prophets before, such as Musa and 'Isa, 'alaihima's-salam, but unlike the perverted remnants of their revelations, Judaism and Christianity. Human modifications over time have changed the teaching of the unity of the Sovereign Lord, demeaning their clear understanding and substituting for it something nearer to the procreation process of human beings. So a biotic son and father relationship and a idolatrous trinity were brought in, not by revelation but by human contrivance. The deen of Allah from its beginnings with Adam to Ibrahim, Musa, 'Isa and Muhammad, salla'llahu 'alaihi wa 'alaihim wa sallam, and thereafter has always been and will remain submission to the Lord Allah alone, and obedience to His Messenger, and obedience to the successors of the Prophet in authority. The first Commandment of the Lord to Musa, 'alaihi's-salam, is, in paraphrase, "Worship Me alone, worship no idols."

'Isa, alaihi's-salam, came to re-establish the knowledge of this tawhid for the Children of Israel, and Muhammad, salla'llahu 'alaihi wa sallam, completed this mission to mankind. The priests and scholars of the religions have, through forgetfulness and error, lost this message or they deliberately altered that which did not suit them.

In Islam this One Lord is known by the Divine Name 'Allah' with which He has named Himself to us. He, being unlike any thing, is over and above any gender of male or female. Allah ta'ala in the Qur'an, the last revealed Book, says:

"Say, 'He is Allah, One:
Allah, the Eternal Absolute;
He begets not, nor is He begotten;
And there is none like unto Him.'"
(Qur'an 112: 1-4)

"As-salamu 'alaikum", with these words a Muslim greets another during the day and the night. It means "peace be on you". Can you think of a better greeting to another in this world of tension and turmoil?

The Arabic word, 'Islam', means submission and surrender and derives from a root which has to do with peace. The essence of peace is in submission to the Lord and to His will, and an expression of His will is the order within His creation. Yes, all the prophets believed in Allah's creation of the cosmos and they expressed that in the languages prevalent in their time and territory. Can there be something in existence without One Who made it Be? Can there be a creation without a Creator?

"He who created the seven heavens, one upon another; no want of proportion will you see in the creation of the most Gracious. So turn your vision again. Do you see any flaw?"
(Qur'an 67: 3)

All that you see or feel, up and around, is running according to a faultless discipline and order. And who but the Creator can bring and maintain that order and balance in the fathomless universe of which the planet earth is no more than an atom. And the humans and other things and beings of the earth are more minute than any planet or star. But thank Allah that He has ordained some power and knowledge to us – the minute atoms of His creation – in His grace. We have to accept that grace in submission and peace and help maintain that balance and discipline by our gifted knowledge. This is the eternal human religion of Allah for human good. It is the way of Unitarianism (Tawhid) and Submission (Islam) for all mankind as revealed through the final Book, the Glorious Qur'an. Others may differ on this premise or even be antagonistic for lack of correct information but what else does mankind need other than peace and tranquillity from its Lord Allah?

The first revelation of Allah came to His last prophet Muhammad, salla'llahu 'alaihi wa sallam, through His angel Jibril on the mount of Hira near Makkah in the month of Ramadan.

> **"Read, in the name of your Lord and Cherisher Who created. He created man out of a leech-like-clot. Read, and your Lord is the most generous, He Who taught by the pen, taught man that which he did not know."**
> (Qur'an 97: 1-5)

Humans are made of clay and are mortal and erring by nature. Man is however endowed with the faculty of love and affection for the Creator and all His creatures. He can decide between right and wrong with their consequent rewards and punishments. He is created to worship one Lord alone and to be right-acting. This worship and right action include not only the five fundamental pillars of Islam – Witnessing, Prayer, Fasting, Zakat and Pilgrimage; but also in doing good deeds and avoiding all wrong.

Muslims also believe that the transitory life on earth is a preparing ground for the permanent life Hereafter. Man is created not only with a body but also with a soul. In this overall context we have to see how Islam treats the environment.

Three things are very clear in Islam based on the revealed Book, the Qur'an, and the Sunnah (the practice of the last prophet, salla'llahu 'alaihi wa sallam, and of his

Khulafa who took the right way). They are:

1. The whole universe is the creation of Allah with a set order and a balance between all things and beings in it. There is an inter-relationship, between man and the Creator, a part of which is that man is the slave of his Lord, and his attributes such as knowledge, seeing and hearing are borrowed from Him. There is an inter-relationship between man and other creatures. We have to maintain all of the above by our tawhid and by our worshipping ('ibadah) Him alone. Allah says this in the Qur'an:

"Glorify the name of your Guardian Lord Most High, Who created, and further, given order and proportion; Who measured and granted guidance; and Who brings out the (green and luscious) pasture, and then makes it swarthy stubble."
(Qur'an 87: 1-5. See also Qur'an 55: 3-9)

2. Man is, if he undertakes this task, a representative (Khalifah) of Allah on earth where he is a trustee of beings and things around him. He is accountable to Allah for the trust (*amanah*) He has reposed in him for the care of his own self and of beings and things around him. Man is mortal and to err is human, so he needs guidance and forgiveness from Allah Who is all-powerful, beneficent and merciful. He has the duty to worship Allah without associating anything with him and if he does that he has the right to expect that Allah will not put him in the Fire. Allah ta'ala says in Qur'an:

"Then We made you the heirs (Khulafa) in the land after them, to see how you behave."
(Qur'an 10: 14 see also 6: 165)

3. Man, being gifted with limited knowledge, needs divine guidance for his own good. He was blessed by Allah's sending the prophets and revealing the books in different ages and places, and it is vital that he lives by that guidance to avoid disaster in this world and the Hereafter. Guidance is not confined to some religious rituals but it is a code of right action to be followed in human life, laid down in the Qur'an and the Sunnah. This code of right action for daily life and for the major and minor events of life is followed by living in true worship, with the best social behaviour rather than private and familial morality, and with the highest ethical values. It is not just a Friday or a Sunday congregational prayer, but it is the following of a code of daily life with full responsibility and accountability to Allah. Allah ta'ala says in the Qur'an:

"O people, worship your Guardian Lord, Who created you and those who came before you that you may become godfearing."
(Qur'an 2: 21 see also 51: 56)

The revelations to earlier prophets may not have categoric or distinct references to all the problems man may face on this earth, but Allah ta'ala says in the Qur'an, the final revealed book:

"We have explained in detail in this Qur'an, for the benefit of mankind, every kind of similitude, but man is, in most things, contentious."
(Qur'an 18: 54)

For the last 1,400 years the Muslims have been taking guidance from the Qur'an, first and foremost in living in a way pleasing to Allah, but also in the fields of science, astronomy, algebra, chemistry, physics, biology, philosophy, ecology and other subjects of mundane and cosmic knowledge. Non-Muslims too have taken some things from the Qur'an, but Allah ta'ala explained in the very beginning of the Book, that it is **"A guidance for the people of taqwa"** (Qur'an 2: 2) and taqwa is fearful awareness of Allah coupled with the action and behaviour that He is pleased with, in other words the shari'ah of Islam and the Sunnah of the Messenger of Allah, salla'llahu 'alaihi wa sallam. Therefore, a non-Muslim who claims to receive guidance from the Qur'an without becoming a Muslim and living by it is not telling the truth, because Islam is the guidance. Maurice Bucaille in *The Bible, the Qur'an and Science*, upholds the concord that exists between the Qur'an and scientific knowledge, as do many other scientists and thinkers.[74]

We must add a caveat to that, however, since science is notoriously fickle and changeable, and to declare a grand harmony between Qur'an and science may be true today but what happens when science changes its mind tomorrow? For example, Newtonian Mechanics is based on a picture that gravity is a force of attraction between masses. It allows very accurate calculations of trajectories and even orbits of spacecraft and other celestial objects, so much so that missions to the planets can be carried out with breathtaking precision. Einstein however, came up with an entirely different picture that gravity is a curvature of space caused by massive objects. It was not just that his picture was more accurate than Newton's, but that Newton's picture was held to be wrong and Einstein's right, and yet Newton's calculations worked impeccably. So if Newton could be wrong but get the right mathematical answers, how do we know that Einstein's also very impressive right answers do not come from a wrong theory? The picture is further complicated by Quantum Mechanics which is trying to show that gravity is a force between particles which is expressed by the exchange of a sub-atomic particle.

Qur'an does not only guide you on the five pillars of Islam, which are part of 'ibadat, the acts of worship, but it incorporates in it divine wisdom on all matters of human concern, most particularly the *mu'amalat*, the daily everyday things of life such as marriage, divorce, trade, war, and bringing up children, etc., and, moreover, even matters such as science, economy, ecology and environment.

We have seen that the message covers the stewardship and the trust, it contains within it compassion, and, by its nature, it deals with conservation, the balance in Allah's creation, it is based on submission and surrender to the Divine, and leads to peace in the human heart in relation to all beings of the universe which are in submission to Allah, and war against the rebellious, disobedient and disbelieving folk. It includes mention of all the bounties of the Lord and indications of how humans must treat water, land, animals, the species, greenery and air. If we follow that path the wastage, mischief, exploitation and imbalance in nature and society, and the pollution in the environment will be well contained by its ethical, social and legal norms.

Conclusion

5.1. Science, Technology and Faith

Science and technology should not be considered our masters and saviours as they are merely human tools.

The Muslims must all unite to save themselves and others from environmental doom, not relying on science and technology, but utilising these tools for achieving our noble objective of stopping the degradation of human beings and the planet.

Science led to the numerous inventions of industrial growth, without scientists considering their impact on all beings and the natural world around them. They upset the balance in nature without realising that environmental degradation has reached to the point that the ecosystem is on the brink of collapse. In modern days many believe that we cannot do without science and modern technology, but we must free ourselves from its yoke of slavery. In our minds we are trapped by their material grip and only an intellectual rearmament, a new social awareness and slavehood to the Divine can save us. Not all scientists are amoral or irreligious, but the ones who do retain some measure of awareness of the unseen and of the divine, must stick to their faith and invite others to divine guidance. That is how Muslims should motivate others to stick to the Truth and the Right.[77-85]

5.2. International Law

The beautiful universe with all the stars and the planets moving in their orderly courses would not be there if one thing was missing. The society that we live in and the land we inhabit would not be peaceful if one thing was missing. The family that we tend with love and responsibility would not be orderly if one thing was missing. The person who is borne in his mother's womb and enjoys a life of vigour and energy on the earth for a determined period only, would not be there if the same thing was missing. That common denominator of all these missing links is nothing but order: the law of the universe, the law of the society, the law of the family and the personal law of good conduct. Awareness and respect for that law and order are what are missing in our intellects. If we know that fundamental law we will respect and obey it for our own benefit and violate it at our peril.

The environmental chaos, with all its prevailing circumstances which we discussed, cannot be led to an orderly and peaceful conclusion without a law and submission to its tenets. That is why the things we agree upon, the things we need to do and the manner in which we have to conduct ourselves in this catastrophe have to be formulated within a legal framework for everyone to respect and follow. The universal law of the cosmos set by Divine Decree we cannot change, nor can we alter the fitrah upon which every living thing is based. But how we conduct ourselves with each of them is our human responsibility, for which we are accountable. The problem of pollution which we face today is local, regional, national and global, so the law of our conduct has to be reflected at all these levels.

The problem we are facing is one caused by our ignoring the set of Divine laws which govern the physical creation, so the law we must follow to restore the balance must itself be a Divine law in harmony with physical law since it is from the same source; no patchwork of human laws will do, and indeed no patchwork of altered, decayed and corrupted remnants of Divine law will do. It is only the law of Islam which fits the bill, as we have said before. If that sounds intolerant, we have also said before that it is the only Divine law which takes account of the fact that before it there were other revelations, and so within the shari'ah of Islam it is permitted for the People of the Book to live by their revelations under the governance of the Muslims. It is the only shari'ah which allows that to happen. If anyone were to call for the coordination of all religious faiths willy nilly in mutual respect, then that is inconceivable but it is possible for Islam to unite peoples of different revelations in the way outlined above, although it is preferable to us that people recognise the truth of the unity of the Divine and of the Message of Muhammad, salla'llahu 'alaihi wa sallam, and become our brothers in Islam. However, it is precisely here that the ayah which is so often quoted in the wrong context is true, **"There is no compulsion (to enter) in(to) the deen,"** (Qur'an 2: 256) which I have here quite deliberately translated with the well-recognised commentary inserted in parentheses. In the deen there is definitely compulsion, for example in the matter of the payment of the zakah, and even in the performance of the prayer; no Muslim is at liberty to exercise freedom of choice in these matters, just as murder, adultery, theft and usury are not a matter of freedom of personal choice and for the individual conscience. But no-one may be compelled to enter into the deen.

As for my non-Muslim reader, when you think about Islam don't ignore it or be carried away by the Western media projection of it as a 'fundamentalist', 'terrorist' or a 'backward' religion. Do think about Islam's role of enlightenment, peace and brotherhood within the Dar al-Islam, an abode of safety to which Muslims invite non-Muslims rather than trying to exclude them, and think about Islam and its environmental message of trusteeship (*amanah*) and balance (*mizan*). Islam is the most powerful moving force for combating the all round pollution threatening our existence at every dimension and level of it. The message of Islam is not only for those who are already Muslims but it is a call and an invitation to the whole of mankind to march together under the banner of "There is no god but Allah and Muhammad is the Messenger of Allah".

It is gratifying to note that the process of environmental awareness has started at various levels to enable one to see within the shari'ah precisely those dynamic elements which are of most relevance in this particular situation. There is little needed immediately other than the implementation of the clear shari'ah on commerce, trade and related matters, and on the more specifically environmental measures.

Outside the Muslim community, local and national laws and regulations of clean water, clean air and pollution free land and atmosphere are rapidly coming into force due to that awareness. But what is lacking is a global legal framework in the binding form of Conventions or Protocols in all fields, and their enforcement by all parties. Some such instruments are already in place, like the Basel Convention of 1989 on the control of trans-boundary movements of hazardous wastes and their disposal, and the Law of the Sea of 1982 controlling pollution in the marine environment and the related land and air, and the Montreal Protocol of 1990, on the ozone layer depletion, with later amendments. The Earth Summit at Rio in 1992 initiated more Conventions on Biodiversity and Climate Change.

However, it is well to bear in mind that the mode of legislation, as it exists on the earth today, is merely the haggling of different parties over their investments and vested interests. It is inconceivable that such a process could deliver mankind from the disaster that they are in. Just imagine that the crew of the Titanic started to debate with the Captain about whom they thought was more important to take into the lifeboats, each man arguing on his own and his relatives' behalfs.

At long last, and in spite of the above mentioned misgivings about their procedures, the UNEP has initiated some steps in the right direction to consolidating and processing the research and study, and towards monitoring global activities to save the environment from further degradation.

Our legal and theological strategy should be to:

1. Review the International Conventions and Protocols on environment within the framework of the shari'ah, which is based on social and humanitarian ethics as discussed above.
2. Make a clear stand as Muslims in opposition to all pollution of the planet and the usury economy which drives that pollution, and very publicly oppose as individuals and groups engagement with every such activity, not only because of the pollution but in obedience to Allah and His Messenger.
3. Become involved in creating societies which embody halal modes of trade, and non-polluting technologies.

5.3. Control in Islam

Many of us, even many renowned scholars (*'ulama*), are not aware, that there are about one hundred ayat of the Noble Qur'an revealed about the environment (*bi'ah*), and that there are even more references in the hadith of the Prophet Muhammad, salla'llahu 'alaihi wa sallam, only a few of which are quoted in this book.

The question of some scientists and ecologists, "What does religion have to do with environmental problems, which are really technical matters?" receives a ready answer from three Islamic fundamentals mentioned above in the chapter on the Ecological Message of Islam. In other words, the whole universe is interconnected, so that each being in it has an effect, one upon the other. You cannot isolate matter from spirit, science from theology, the animate from the inanimate or humans from other living beings. Allah is the Lord and Sustainer of this interdependent and orderly, universal cosmic system. It is said that His Lordship, which in Arabic is called *rububiyyah*, is by means of the interdependence of His creations and creatures.

You may reject this balance and order for a while as did Qabil, Fir'awn, Nimrod, Goliath, Chengiz Khan, Darwin or Marx, but don't you know of their ultimate fate? Allah says in the Qur'an:

> **"It is Allah who causes the seed grain and the date stone to split and sprout. He causes the living to issue from the dead. And He is the One to cause the dead to issue from the living. That is Allah: then how are you deluded away from the truth?"**
> (Qur'an 6: 96)

As rational beings we don't believe in a creation of the earth by chance – a 'big bang' – nor to the theory that natural resources are limitless and man can dominate them as he likes for his prosperity and development ignoring the rights of the weak and of animals and other beings:

> **"Allah is the One Who raised the heavens without any pillars that you can see; then He estab-**

lished Himself on the throne. He has subjected the sun and the moon, each one runs its course for a term appointed. He regulates all affairs, explaining the signs in detail, that you may believe with certainty in the meeting with your Lord. And it is He Who has spread out the earth, and set thereon mountains standing firm, and (flowing) rivers, and fruit of every kind He made in pairs, two and two."
(Qur'an 13: 2-3)

"To Him is the primal origin of the heavens and the earth. When He creates a thing, He has just to say to it 'Be', and it is."
(Qur'an 2: 117 and see also Qur'an 6: 23).

The revelations made to the ancient prophets before the Children of Israel and of their stock also revealed the same reality of the Creation, but then later they were altered by humans substituting 'dominion' in place of the 'trusteeship' of man. Islam unequivocally gives man only trusteeship of natural resources and of the creation, and not 'dominion' or 'domination' as already discussed above. Even were the ayat where Allah ta'ala mentions human possession of the kingdom, for example, **"You give the kingdom to whomever You will "** (Qur'an 3: 26) to be understood in the sense of 'dominion', yet uppermost in the mind of every Muslim is the simple concept that he is totally responsible to Allah and accountable for every action be it great and small. Some of the great kings and khalifahs of the Muslims have been much more afraid of Allah and His accounting than have even some of the great Awliya' of Allah. All men and Muslims must take care of themselves and the environment. This trusteeship is the mission of the people of Islam, not dominion, domination, nor exploitation of men and resources, of East and West. Waste not, but use and preserve. The guidance of Allah in the Qur'an is:

> **"O children of Adam, wear your beautiful apparel at every time and place of prayer: eat and drink but waste not by excess, for Allah does not love the wasters."**
> (Qur'an 7: 31 and also see Qur'an 6: 141)

One very relevant hadith of the Prophet, salla'llahu 'alaihi wa sallam, is:

> "The merit of utilisation is in the benefit it yields, in proportion to its harm."
> (Tirmidhi)[26]

One of the early Muslim scholars, Abul Faraj wrote:

> "People don't in fact own things, for the real owner is their Creator; they only enjoy the usufruct, subject to the divine law."[76]

So the admonition comes to the children of Adam to maintain the balance (*mizan*) for themselves and for others. (Qur'an 55: 3-10)

The specific subjects of land ownership and use, rights and duties pertaining to water and air, treatment of animals, and forestry, etc., have been all dealt with in Shari'ah Law. As to man, animals, water and plants, Allah says:

> **"He Who has made for you the earth like a carpet spread out; has enabled you to go about therein by roads (and channels), and has sent down water from the sky. With it have We produced diverse pairs of plants each separate from the others. Eat (for yourselves) and pasture your**

cattle: verily in this are signs for men endued with understanding."
(Qur'an 20: 53-54)

As to water, man and animals, Allah, glorious and exalted is He, says:

"And Allah has created every animal from water: of them there are some that creep on their bellies; some that walk on two legs and some that walk on four. Allah creates what He wills; for verily Allah has power over all things."
(Qur'an 24: 45)

Similarly, animals and birds are not treated in isolation or as beasts of prey only but are treated in the Qur'an as integral parts of the communities of living beings, long before the movement for the 'Prevention of Cruelty to Animals' was born:

"There is not an animal (that lives) on the earth, nor a being that flies on its wings, but (that it forms part of) communities like you. Nothing have We omitted from the Book, and they (all) shall be gathered to their Lord at the end."
(Qur'an 6: 38)

Water being the lifeline for all beings, its reckless use, waste or pollution cannot be allowed just for an alleged material development or prosperity, no matter how many market forces may command you. Water for agriculture, industry and commerce or for personal use must never be wasted. Prayer five times a day is obligatory upon Muslims, and for that one has to prepare oneself by performing a washing with water (*wudu*), or even a thorough washing of the entire body (*ghusl*), or, as is permitted to the sick and those who cannot find water a dry wash (*tayammum*). All of these must be performed without extravagance or waste. The reply of the Prophet Muhammad, salla'llahu 'alaihi wa sallam, to one of his companion's (Sa'd, radiya'llahu 'anhu) query, "Can there be waste in washing for the prayer?" was that he said emphatically, "Yes, even if you are beside flowing water." (*Mishkat al-Masabih*).

As to the wind and air Allah, the Mighty and Majestic, says:

> **"It is Allah Who sends forth the winds, so that they raise up the clouds, and We drive them to a land that is dead, and revive the earth therewith after its death."**
> (Qur'an 35: 9)

We have discussed above the extent of the damage man has done to forests, soil, water and air, creating the greenhouse effect, acid-rain and depletion of the ozone layer. It was not until very recently that environmental activists expressed concern, and laws and protocols are now being framed to undo the damage. But Islamic legislation on forests, land and wildlife were in place 1,400 years ago, and even before that in the revelations accorded to some previous prophets; but rarely noticed by us. A hadith of the Prophet Muhammad, salla'llahu 'alaihi wa sallam, is that he is reported to have said:

> "The world is sweet and green, and Allah has appointed you as His Khalifahs (trustees) over it to see how you act."
> (Muslim)[26]

In another hadith there is that:

> "If any one plants a tree or sows a field, and men,

beasts or birds eat from it, it is considered as a *sadaqah* on his part."
(*Musnad* Imam Ahmad)[26]

As to the Qur'an we already have quoted sections above, and there are many similar ayat in other surahs for guidance on environmental protection. The first revelation of the Qur'an – Surah 96, al-'Alaq and the first Surah of the Qur'an – al-Fatihah, speak of man, the worlds and their Creator and the One Who disposed them in balance and order. In the former, Allah ta'ala says:

"Recite in the name of your Lord Who creates; creates man from a clot. Recite and your Lord is the Most Generous Who teaches by the pen, teaches man that which he did not know."
(Qur'an 96: 1-5)

So Allah the exalted mentions the wonder of His creating man from a mere clot, a thing which clings and hangs suspended, as does the embryo in the womb, and then Allah ta'ala brought him out as a knowing creature whom He teaches by the pen.

In al-Fatihah, Allah the Glorious says:

"Praise belongs to Allah, the Lord of the worlds,"
(Qur'an 1: 1)

He is the Lord, meaning the God (i.e. the One worshipped); the Lord; the Owner; and the One Who puts right. All of these meanings are in "The Lord of the worlds" but the meaning of "the God" is the most correct because of its being particularly for Allah, exalted is He. He is the Lord of "the worlds" all of them including the worlds of the animals and insects, the fishes and the birds, the inner and outer worlds.

The beginning, the development and the end, everything

in Islam speaks of order and harmony. Allah orders all men to preserve the set balance and order in the creation with submission and peace as His trustees, however it is only the Muslims who 'submit' to His commands. This is the clear call and guidance of Islam on life and environment. We erring mortals disobey it only at our peril. We must turn back and not repeat our disobedience, so that He can forgive us. He is most kind and merciful to those who believe and turn to Him from their wrong action. (See Qur'an 2: 109, 4: 48)

When Abu Bakr, the first Khalifah of Islam, sent an expedition to Muta to preach the message and fight for it, if necessary, he gave specific instructions to his troops:

"Don't cut down trees and don't kill animals except for food (in the enemy territory)."
(At-Tabari)

Later, the Muslim army which conquered the Byzantine troops in Syria had the same instructions. This clearly shows that not only do Muslims recognise that plants and animals have to be conserved, but that Allah confers the trusteeship of the earth and of all His creation upon man which is something that the Muslims clearly accept, contrary to our present materialistic behaviour of domination over the earth and its resources. Allah will also see how we conduct ourselves in the light of this guidance. The Qur'an is specific on the issue, and in it Allah says:

"Then We appointed you after them to be khalifahs (successors) in the earth so We might observe how you would act."
(Qur'an 10: 14 see also 2: 30, and 6: 165)

In Islam, man is seen only as Allah's representative (*khalifah*) holding a trust (*amanah*), and this is the highest and most exalted position in the creation, since the representative of a Mighty King has a noble place. Man however is not himself a great king and so must not loot or plunder the earth and its resources like the capitalists and communists do. Especially important to ecologists and to our continuance on earth are non-renewable global resources. Unscrupulous financial magnets destroy and plunder non-renewable natural resources at will, but a hopeful sign today is that some ethically-conscious administrators decorate gardens and parks with natural greenery.

Hyde Park, Regents Park and Kew Gardens of London used to attract me most when I was a student there. Whenever I am in London, like millions more, I enjoy the gardens, lakes and blue skies, but unfortunately even they are becoming polluted today. Whenever I visit Tokyo or Washington the green parks and gardens there too attract me most. Tokyo, a most crowded city with all its skyscrapers, industrial fumes and hectic communication networks, would be lifeless without its thousands of gardens. The magnificent Imperial Palace garden which covers over 100 hectares of land, Hibya Park with flowers and fountains in the city centre, Hamariku Garden out in Tokyo Bay with the sea-waters coming in and out and the Otani Gardens, are only a few enjoyable parks which are worthy of mention. In the luscious Otani Gardens of Tokyo, Hyde Park of London and the City Garden of Addis Ababa, you can relax and even be a guest at garden weddings on weekends. The traditional gardens, lakes and forests in and around Peking city (now Beijing) also attract visitors and residents alike.

But when you enter the city of Madinah, in the heart of the dry and sandy Saudi Arabian desert, where the Prophet Muhammad, salla'llahu 'alaihi wa sallam, lived and lies buried, you cannot but be surprised. The date trees, grapevines, water melon fields, green gardens, flowery plants and green grasses in and around the city live up to the Prophet's description of the earth as "green and beautiful." For 1,400 years the desert cities of Makkah, Madinah and Taif have been maintained as green and peaceful cities following his tradition. These are becoming even greener nowadays with abundant fruits, flowers and vegetables.

While I was in charge, with Ahmad Khalawi, of building Saudia City in Jeddah for the employees of Saudi Arabian Airlines, I made a point of making the city green, following the same tradition. Fruit trees were specially planted so that men and birds could derive benefit. Saudi Developer Muhammad Amoudi and British consultant Jerry Wingate rendered all their support in our effort to bring about environmental greenery. One can enjoy with delight that green oasis today on the sandy shores of the Red Sea.

The divine code legislated for human conduct also protects the smallest of the species or animals be they hidden from human eyes within the hardest stones, deepest water or dense forests.

The Prophet, salla'llahu 'alaihi wa sallam, said:

> "An ant had bitten an (earlier) Prophet and he ordered that the colony of ants should be burnt. Allah revealed to him, 'Because of an ant's bite have you burnt a community from amongst the communities which sings My glory?'"
> (Muslim and Bukhari)

In another hadith, the Prophet, salla'llahu 'alaihi wa sallam, said:

> "A woman was punished because she had kept a cat tied until it died; and she was thrown into the Fire. She had not provided it with food or drink and had not freed it, so that it could (at least) eat the insects of the earth."
> (Muslim)

He also said to his companions that there is a reward for serving every living animal. (Muslim)[26]

The Prophet, salla'llahu 'alaihi wa sallam, established inviolable zones in and around Makkah and Madinah 1,400 years ago and they are still respected by Muslims today. Trees, shrubs or vegetation cannot be cut nor can wild animals be hunted or disturbed there according to the Sunnah.

A camel was tied up without any food or drink by a man whom the Prophet, salla'llahu 'alaihi wa sallam, asked: "Don't you fear Allah regarding this animal which Allah has given into your possession? It has complained to me that you keep it hungry and burden it to the point of fatigue?"

(Abu Dawud)[26]

The Prophet, salla'llahu 'alaihi wa sallam, asked even his beloved wife A'ishah, radiya'llahu 'anha, to treat an untrained camel with kindness, and not with severity. He ordered one of his companions to return a mother bird to its nest to the very place from where it had been taken. He told them that a woman who gave water to a very thirsty dog earned forgiveness for her wrong actions. (Muslim and Bukhari)[26]

Let it be repeated how the Prophet, salla'llahu 'alaihi wa sallam, showed concern for animals, birds and humans. He is reported to have said:

> "There is no Muslim who plants a tree or sows a field, and then a man, animal or bird eats from it, but it will be counted as a sadaqah for him."
> (Muslim)

Some people worship terrestrial powers or mighty animals or birds as their gods. Islam gives them their due meaning and measure in the entire creation without idolising them or their abuse or destruction. Some of the surahs of the Qur'an have even been titled with names of animals and living creatures. Allah ta'ala shows how man can benefit from creatures, and draw lessons from natural things, without either misusing them or, at the other extreme, idolising them. There are the surahs of al-Baqarah (the Cow), al-An'am (the Cattle), an-Nahl (the Bee), an-Naml (the Ant), al-'Ankabut (the Spider) and al-Fil (the Elephant). Do not worship or idolise them, but take lessons from them and derive benefits both from the creatures themselves and from wisdom which can be learnt from reflecting on them and on the creation. Never waste or misuse these creatures which are such gifts from the Creator to us, but rather conserve and protect them as fellow communities and slaves of the Divine Lord of all the worlds. Also, do not idealise or idolise nature, as is possible in the so-called 'Gaia' belief, but conserve and protect the natural world of the fitrah, to keep the balance set by the Divine Decree. Allah the Exalted says:

> **"And truly in cattle you will find an instructive Sign; from what is in their bodies, between excretion and blood, We produce for you drink, milk (which is) pure and agreeable to those who drink it. And from the fruit of the date palm and the vine you extract strong drink and wholesome food: behold in this also is a Sign for those who are wise. And your Lord taught the bee to build its cells in hills, on trees and in habitations. Then 'Eat of all the produce (of the earth), and follow the ways of your Lord made smooth'. There issues from within their bodies a drink of varying colours, wherein is healing for men. Verily in this is a Sign for those who give thought."**
>
> (Qur'an 16: 66-69)

We conclude this topic, much neglected by men and even by the Muslims, with a narration of importance in the Book itself. Allah the Mighty and Majestic tells us, quoting a Prophet, 'alaihi's-salam, speaking to his people:

> **"This she-camel of Allah is a sign to you; leave her to graze in Allah's earth, and let her come to no harm, or you will be seized with a grievous punishment."**
> (Qur'an 7: 73 and see also 26: 155)

The prophet was Salih, 'alaihi's-salam, the people were Thamud and the location was in the north of Arabia. Madain Salih is to the south of another historic location, Petra in Jordan. It is where the prosperous people of Thamud were vanquished for disobeying Allah by destroying one of His creatures rebelliously when they had been warned not to do it. This warning was repeated in the Qur'an twenty-two times (in Surahs 7, 11, 25, 26, 27, 29, 41, 51, 54, 69, 85, 89, 91) but went unheeded by the arrogant greedy people of Thamud. Poetically we could say that the industrially and agriculturally developed people of today are also ignoring repeated warnings not to destroy Allah's creatures. If anyone has any iota of doubt about the lessons of history and of the reality of divine punishment, he can visit Madain Salih today. Allah punished the people through a natural disaster, but you can see the traces of their material progress in the remains of the burnt mountains and sandy rocks. Of course, the significance of the story is not in the cruelty they showed the beast, but in their defiance of their prophet. Yet the present desecration of the earth and destruction of species is, in its way, a defiance of divine warning and of prophethood, so the story holds true to our present situation.

This lesson applies not only to cruelty to animals, but can be extended to inhumane treatment of all living things created by Allah with their natural rights and obligations to themselves and to each other – the interrelatedness which is a part of the balance in the creation "in due measure and proportion", as repeated in the Qur'an. This is not our discovery, nor a discovery of modern environmentalists, but it came down in divine revelations 1,400 years ago. We quote here one more of many ayat in the Qur'an:

> **"Do they not see how many of those before them We destroyed of generations We had established on the earth, in strength such as We have not given to you?"**
> (Qur'an 6: 6)

Early Muslim thinkers like al-Jahiz of the 8th century and 'Izzu'd-din ibn Abdi's-Salam of the 13th century left their treatises on the treatment of animals. Ibn Abdi's-Salam, in his works, formulated a code for the good treatment of animals long before the West thought of animal and human rights. He wrote:

> "Know that Allah created His creatures and made them dependent on each other, so that each group would support the welfare of each other."
> (*Desert Reclamation and Islamic Law*, The Muslim Scientist, Vol. 2 1982)[76]

Wastage is prohibited in Islam and those who waste (*mubadhdhireen*) have been likened to the brothers of the accursed shaytan. This applies to any kind of waste and misuse, and is a metaphor which must be realised by the consumption-happy throwaway societies of the North and South.

Another thing which is strongly prohibited in Islam is corruption or mischief (*fasad*). This term applies in the realm of environment as in any other field of life. Thus wasting or damaging any food, water, forest, land or air and any creature of Allah is strictly and repeatedly forbidden in the Book:

> **"O children of Adam: Eat and drink but do not waste by excess, for Allah does not love the wasters."**
> (Qur'an 7: 31)

About corruption also we repeat only a few ayat of many in the Qur'an:

> **"Corruption has appeared on land and sea because of that which the hands of men have earned, that He may give them a taste of some of their deeds, in order that they may turn back (from wrong action)."**
> (Qur'an 30: 41)

> **"Do not mischief on the earth, after it has been set in order, but call on Him with fear and longing, for the mercy of Allah is close to those who do good."**
> (Qur'an 7: 56)

The world is full of corruption today perpetrated by humans themselves on all fronts, and what more do we need to prove that assertion than the highly polluted global environment which is heavily contaminated with material impurities, but also with corruption, injustice, exploitation and finally genocidal massacre.

Allah the Creator has set a balance in His entire creation, and humans should not corrupt or pollute that balance by their misdeeds. As the balance in creation means that the creatures are interrelated, and every one in turn has a unique relationship with their Creator, any pollution or damage will earn dire consequences for His creation in this world and in the world Hereafter. Whether this pollution is done in the name of progress, development, revolution or technology we are answerable to our Lord, no less than to our society, for damaging that necessary balance. Today we are sitting on the brink of a major environmental disaster created by human actions. Either we turn from our wrong actions and amend our behaviour or we will meet the doom as previous civilisations did.

Amongst other natural resources, the gifts of Allah entrusted to man to use as trustee, land and air need special mention. According to the Shari'ah land is primarily divided into three categories: developed (*'amir*), undeveloped (*mawat*) and protected (*harim*). The rights of use were detailed in this law 1,400 years ago, which is still followed to some extent in Arab countries including Saudi Arabia. Other Muslim countries of Asia, Africa and Europe followed the principles but Western conquest and dominance changed it to a great extent.

Similarly Shari'ah has also legislation for the utilisation of the natural resources of land and water. Land, according to Shari'ah, is not only soil or barren fields, rather it also consists of grassy soil, sandy deserts, rainforests, deciduous and coniferous forests, oases, habitations, mountains and hills. Each one has its own characteristics set in the creation by divine measure. Man can use and enjoy them as Allah's trustee, with necessary care given to animals, birds and other beings.

Even in the deserts on the Asian, African, Australian and American continents, hundreds of plants, animals and species live. The tropical forests of South America, Africa and Asia cover about 7% of the land but contain over 50% of the animals, birds and other species. Allah provides sustenance to each of them, including worms and insects inside the hardest stones and softest water. Man cannot claim 'dominion' over them nor can he crush or liquidate them under his feet for his merriment, comfort or development.

Man is answerable not only to human law but to the divine reckoning, according to how he behaves in accordance with the Shari'ah or counter to it.

This Shari'ah law divides mineral resources into two categories: open (*dhahir*) and concealed (*batin*). Islamic jurists have discerned various principles from the concrete cases which govern matters of both private and public use. The fundamental principle applying to all these minerals is in accepting the ownership of Allah, and in consequence the position that man occupies merely as a trustee, causing no misuse or wastage while using the minerals, causing no harm to the rights of others and payment of Zakat on its income to the Khalifah and his Amirs for them to discharge to the needy beneficiaries.

Muslim writers on modern ecology and environment are not many, though the Qur'an and the Sunnah speak volumes. However, Yasin Dutton, in *Islam and Ecology*, a collection of essays and articles by different Muslim authors published by Cassell, London, pp. 51-67, briefly outlines this law in his article. Othman Llewellyn also deals with the position of desert reclamation and conservation in Islam in that book.[63]

One hadith of the last Prophet Muhammad, salla'llahu 'alaihi wa sallam, needs to be repeated here with respect to caring for the land and desert:

> "Whoever brings dead land to life, for him there is a reward for it, and whatever creature seeking food eats of it, then it shall be reckoned as a voluntary act of sadaqah for him.
> (*Mishkat Al-Masabih*)

As representatives (khalifahs) and trustees of Allah, we have a duty to look after ourselves and the creation around us, which was entrusted to us for our use and care within the limits prescribed by Him. Allah, exalted is He and glorious, says:

> **"Allah commands you to render back your trusts to those to whom they are due; and when you judge between people that you judge with justice. How excellent is the teaching He gives you! For Allah is One Who hears and sees all things."** (Qur'an 4: 58-9 and see also 8: 27)

Besides the fundamentals of the ecological message of Islam we must also act according to the following:

a. We should plant crops, trees, and grasses, and enjoy their fruits, fragrance and benefits, but not wastefully fell fruit trees and living trees or damage the green earth.

b. We may harvest the wood but not lay waste the forest or subsoil, rather conserve the soil, forests and greenery around us.

c. We may drink and use to irrigate – but not pollute or waste – waters of taps, ponds, lakes, wells, rivers and seas.

d. We may use land but not wrongfully and injuriously trespass, we must not over-graze, poison, desertify or damage it, above or beneath the ground.

e. We may use essential air but not pollute or overheat it with gases and chemicals used in factories, agriculture and transport vehicles.

f. We must not waste anything, but reduce, reuse and recycle our wastes keeping ourselves and things and beings around us clean and productive. Muslims had more than a thousand years of civilisation built on not wasting, and on reusing materials the modern age regards as waste matter.

g. We may use non-renewable resources, but not exploit or dominate them without consideration for others and with no concern for the future, and we must

conserve commercial, industrial and domestic power.
h. We must cultivate and conserve fishes, birds, animals and species.
i. We should stop smoking and use no alcoholic drinks or addictive drugs even for holidays and festivities, for these are some of the pollutants of our inner metabolic environments as is only too well authenticated physiologically.
j. We must grow more pollution-free healthy food. Where organic meats are considered then halal meat is the royal crown, combining, as halal slaughter does, mercy for the animal and physiological health for the meat-eater (this cannot apply in anyway to the so-called 'halal meat' which issues from the vast automated slaughterhouses of today, and which is indistinguishable in almost every sense from all the other meat that comes out of the same slaughterhouses). We must also see that there is a just economic system in place that will allow the equitable distribution of healthy food and not save it for a technocratic elite with the income to pay for health as a super luxury.
k. We must educate people in a social family planning, free of abortion except perhaps in those exceptional cases where life is threatened, and free of sodomy, which is clearly not an act of love but of aggressive domination and conquest, and free of self-abuse, the last resort of the lonely and neurotic, and build up a family integration of love and affection.
l. We must, as societies, give up exploitation, corruption, mischief, violence and vices, for those are the destructive pollutants of our societies which are infinitely more serious than the chemicals we ingest in our food or breathe in our air, because the former kill the hearts while the latter only kill the bodies. There is no way to the above except by keeping our trusts both with Allah (our covenants with Him) and with His crea-

tures.

This is the principle of moderation, the middle course (*as-sirat al-wusta*) as prescribed in Islam, which we all should follow without hesitation.

Balanced Control in Islam

The whole universe whose Lord (Rabb) is Allah is set in motion by His decree. Allah also set it in a natural balance, and the manifestation of that in each of His creatures is known as '*fitrah*'. This planet earth of ours is only one of nine such planets known in our solar system. There may be many more – according to scientists possibly billions more – of such solar systems in the universe. They are all unarguably interrelated, and they exist in a state of fitrah set by Allah in His decree. Man, who is as if running away from his own fitrah, his own natural condition, ought not interfere with natural fitrah, but nevertheless seems bent on doing so.

The Qur'an mentions the wind and cloud that revive life in the dead earth with rainwater, in Surahs 6, 30 and 35. This mention has a spiritual effect on those who reflect with gratitude on Allah's bounties, and on those who appreciate the balance and order of the creation. The air that man breathes has been severely contaminated with toxic gases by man himself in his ignorance and arrogance. The greenhouse effect, acid-rain, the widening hole in the ozone layer, many droughts and floods, new plagues of apparently previously unknown incurable diseases and other supposedly 'natural' disasters are all mainly due to the environmental catastrophe created by man. The oxygen and nitrogen in the air in a "due measure and proportion" support life in all living beings, This measure is maintained by the order inbuilt by the Lord in land, sea, water and atmosphere. Man cannot create that measure in nature nor could any accidental evolution set such a balance and order in place, but, however, human actions can damage or destroy that measure by the malignant power of the brilliant but often twisted intellect gifted to man.

The Lord has given humans the intelligence to find out the proportion of natural gases in the surface of the planet earth. The atmosphere extends up to 15 km above the ground, the troposphere reaches to about 16 km over the equator and 8 km over the poles, the stratosphere attains between 16 to 50 km, and the mesosphere and thermosphere arrive to 50 km and above.

Gases like carbon dioxide and methane trap and absorb the heat of the sun in the troposphere with the consequence commonly known as the Greenhouse Effect. Gases like ozone absorb the ultraviolet radiation of the sun acting as a protective shield in the stratosphere. Too much burning of fossil fuels and CFC gases has already punched a hole in this protective shield, baring the earth to UV radiation harmful to living beings. This hole was detected over Antarctica around the pole and its continually expanding size is now estimated to be bigger than the United States. Undisturbed the temperatures in these spheres vary according to the normal interaction of the forces of nature, but human acts are grossly disturbing its balance. Allah says in the Glorious Qur'an:

> **"And the firmament has He raised high, and He has set up the balance in order that you may not transgress (due) balance. So establish weight with justice and fall not short in the balance."**
> (Qur'an 55: 7-9 and also see 54: 49 and 67: 3)

But we humans in our insatiable material greed and egocentric pride of our intellects have demonstrated our anti-intellectual stupidity and totally damaged the environment exposing the entire globe to an unprecedented danger. To be rescued from it we have to submit to the rule of the One, the Lord Allah and to His guidance, turn away from our scientific arrogance and our wrong actions, give up political domination and economic exploitation for a pollution-free world in every dimension of our existence, change to sustainable global development, i.e. an ethical and divine-centred one with a profit-sharing welfare economy rather than a usurious exploitative one, and lead right-acting lives of balance, peace and productivity as faithful trustees of Allah.

This is the clear environmental message of Islam for mankind to be saved from the catastrophe. Muslims have to act on this message themselves not in isolation or conflict but as a united Ummah living in close cooperation. There is no other deen acceptable to Allah than Islam, and there is no conceivable salvation for humanity in our present predicament except Islam. That is because a people who know they have a reckoning with their Lord and then an eternity either in the Garden or the Fire, will step lightly on the earth and beware of what they consume and of what footsteps they leave behind them. The Muslims have to show in practice that Islam is not just following some rituals but is a whole code of life including, as a natural consequence of its worship of and obedience to Allah, the preservation and improvement of the environment. Dr. Abdullah Omar Nasseef, former Secretary General of the Muslim World League and the vice chairman of Saudi Majlis ash-Shura, in the Assissi Declaration held that:

> "Muslims need to return to this nexus of values, this way of understanding themselves and their environment. The notions of unity, trusteeship and accountability should not be reduced to matters of personal piety; they must guide all aspects of their life and work. Shari'ah should not be relegated just to issues of crime and punishment, it must also become the vanguard for environmental legislation."[53]

After going through the techno-scientific and socioeconomic data and analysing the theological and social background it was not easy to come to this conclusion. But we have a consensus, not a conflict, that a consequence of all following divine revelation is the preservation and not the destruction of the environment. The damage that we all have done by any false or mistaken idea of the human role in the creation has to be remedied by us jointly and globally. The Lord is kind and merciful so He will surely accept our sincere regret and turning away from the wrong we have done, if we resolve not to repeat the wrongs:

> **"If any one does evil or wrongs his own soul but afterwards seeks Allah's forgiveness, he will find Allah oft- forgiving, most merciful."**
> (Qur'an 4: 110, and see also 4: 48, 42: 5, 53: 32, 57: 21)

This will necessitate a common strategy to be developed by the Muslims with a firm determination to work together giving up jealousy, hatred and antagonism towards each other. There should be a compact of Muslims treating science and technology not as masters nor even as tools of sustainable development. The Muslims when they lived in obedience to Allah as an Ummah under the command of a Khalifah, and not as scattered private individuals, lived lives that were the envy of their ages and our still the envy of knowledgeable historians. Our common goal is to be pleasing to Allah in this world and to gaze on His Countenance in the world Hereafter. We can and shall control the environmental pollution unitedly because our goal is not in this world, and it is the people who are obsessed only with this world who are destroying the earth, even by the very efforts that they loudly declare to be for reform. Allah ta'ala says:

> **"And when it was said to them 'Do not work corruption in the land', they say, 'We are only putting things right.'"**
> (Qur'an 2: 10)

This is perhaps the unique destiny of the utilitarians and those who so slavishly imitate them in this age. Their metaphor is the missionary who trekked thousands of miles through the jungle to bring the "Good News" to some pagans living in near fitrah in the jungle, and unbeknownst to the missionary himself he carries some utterly harmless little virus against which the natives have no defence and which exterminates them!

It is understanding this powerful ayat, which Allah the Glorious and Exalted has placed almost at the very beginning of His revelation, that certainly frees the Muslim from any desire to corrupt but also any need to reform anything whatsoever, since he sees clearly from the ayah that the people who think they are the reformers are the corrupters. It frees him from any desire except to please his Lord in the company of those who live to please their Lord. Living thus they will not pollute and will not waste and they will care for all things and beings as trustees of Allah.

BIBLIOGRAPHY

1. Oxford, Cambridge or Webster Dictionaries.
2. *Community Ecology*, R.E. Ricklefs, New York.
3. *Eco Wars*, D. Day, London.
4. *Deep Ecology*. W. David, New York.
5. *Natural Disasters – Acts of God or Acts of Man?* London.
6. WHO Reports, 1990-6.
7. *Toxic Chemicals*, Dr. Ghazi Al Hazim, Jeddah.
8. *The Earth in the Balance*, Al Gore, London.
9. *Impact & Explosion*, Dr. M.U. Bangash, London.
10. UNEP Reports, 1990-6.
11. GEMS Report, 1995.
12. *The Monthly Minaret*, Los Angeles & International Committee for Farakkah Barrage, New York.
13. *The Ganges Water Dispute*, B. M. Abbas, Dhaka.
14. *Farakkah: A Gordian Knot*, S. S. Sharma, Calcutta.
15. *India's Farakkah Barrage*, M. T. Hussain, London.
16. *Nationalism or Islam*, Akhtaruddin Ahmad, New York.
17. *Planet Earth in Jeopardy*, Lydia Dotto, London.
18. *Kuwait Oil Fire*, Dr. T. Hussain, Oxford.
19. The Noble Qur'an, Arabic & translations of Allama

Yusuf Ali & Marmaduke Pickthall.
20. *The Bible*, translations of King James Authorised Version & Authorised American Version.
21. *Saving our Planet*, UNEP Report, 1991.
22. Daily Arab News, 1991, Jeddah.
23. *Rain Forest Politics*, P. Hurst, London.
24. *The World Conservation Strategy*, IUCN, Paris.
25. *Bio Diversity*, Raven &Wilson, Washington & *The Earth in Transition*, Woodwell, Cambridge.
26. The Six Sahih Hadith Collections, Arabic & Translations.
27. *The Expanding Circle: Ethics & Ecology*, New York
28. *Small is Beautiful*, E. F. Schumacher, London.
29. *GAIA*, J. Lovelock, Oxford.
30. *Beyond the Limits*, Meadows & Randers & *Imperilled Planet*, *Earthscan*, London.
31. World Bank Reports on Environment, !991-6.
32. *The Green House Effect*, T. Hewat & *The Green Home*, K. Christensen, London.
33. *Soil Erosion by Water*, FAO, Rome.
34. *The Natural Alien, Humankind & Environment*, Toronto.
35. *The Acid Rain Controversy*, N. B. Dudley, London.
36. *Downwind, Acid Rain Story, Environment of Credit*, Ottawa.
37. UN Environmental Programme Report, Nairobi.
38. *Limits of Growth*, Club of Rome.
39. *It's a Matter of Survival*, Gordon & Suzuki, London.
40. *Vital Signs*, World Watch Institute, Washington.
41. *Eco Wars*, D. Day, London.
42. *Rehabilitating Damaged Ecosystems*, John Cairns, London.
43. *Our Drowning World*, Anthony Miller, London.
44. *No More War*, Linus Pauling, New York. (*Nuclear and Future Generations*, Routley, Harrisberg.)
45. *Infant Mortality & Nuclear Power Generation*, Sternglass, Hamburg.

46. *Effects of Low Level Environmental Radiation*, Illinois.
47. *Desertification of Arid Lands*, H. E. Drenge, London.
48. *The Threatening Deserts*, A. Graingeh, London.
49. *Deserts*, P. Meigs, UNESCO.
50. *Sands of Change*, Dr. Mustafa Tolba, New York, Nairobi.
51. *Habitat in Crisis*, Paul Ehrlick, London & New York.
52. *The World Conservation of Nature*, IUCN, Paris.
53. *The Assissi Declaration*, 1986, Italy & *The Ohito Declaration*, Japan & Britain, 1995.
54. *Philosophy of Technology*, F. Ferre, New Jersey.
55. *The Holiday Makers*, J. Krippendorf, London.
56. *The Golden Hordes*, L. Turner, London.
57. *Marxism & Islam*, Dr. Abdullah O. Naseef, Jeddah. US News and World report, April 13, 1992 and E.D. Bradley.
58. *Smoking & Your Heart*, British Heart Foundation, London.
59. *Shisha Smoking in Arabia*, Jeddah.
60. *The Third Revolution*, P. Harrison, New York & London.
61. *Truth about the Ozone Hole*, O. H. Scotsman, C.R. Mecoso, J.D. Farrara, A. Edmond, J. Walter, J. Gribbin, N. Booth.
62. *Religions & Spiritual Perspective*, M.T. Mahdi, Cairo.
63. *Islam & Ecology*, F. Khalid, London.
64. *Ethics & Agenda 21*, Dr. N.J. Brown,
65. *Judaism & Ecology*, N. Solomon, London.
66. *Christianity & Ecology*, London.
67. *Save the Earth*, World Watch Institute, Washington.
68. *Eastern Religions & Western Thoughts*, Dr. Radha-krisnan, Oxford.
69. *Community Bio-Diversity*, WWF Report on India, 1990.
70. *The Greening of a Red*, Malcolm MacEwen, London.
71. *Environmental Policy in USSR*, C.E. Zeigler, Boston.
72. *Destruction of Nature in the Soviet Union*, B. Kamarov, New York.

73. *Truth about the Ozone Hole*, Simon & Schuster, Oxford.
74. *The Bible, Qur'an & Science*, Maurice Bucaille, Karachi & Jeddah. The verses from Qur'an and Science, Nurbani, Istanbul.
75. *Animal Rights*, Abu Faraj & Abdus Salam, Cairo.
76. *Desert Reclamation & Islamic Law*, Abdus Salam, Cairo.
77. *The Right & the Good*, Rosino, Oxford.
78. *Environmental Ethics*, D. A. Simmons, Chicago.
79. *The Illusion of Progress*, L. Brown, New York.
80. *Thinking & Deciding*, Cambridge.
81. *Caring for the Earth*, IUCN, UNEP & WWF for Nature, M. Bezley.
82. *Avoiding Social & Ecological Disaster*, R. Bahro, London.
83. *Preserving the Global Environment*, J.J. Matthews, New York.
84. *Interaction of Desertification & Climate*, UNEP & WMO.
85. *Religion & Environment*, L. Wilkinson, New York.
86. *African Report*, A. Shephard. *How to Make Desert*, C. Zimmer; *Shifting Sands*, H. Bregne
87. *Dry Lands and Deserts*, UNESCO
88. *Progress in Desert Research*, L. Belkofsky
89. Publications of International Society of Environmental Ethics, Sweden.
90. *The Greening of a Red*, M. McEwen, London.

Appendices

Appendix 1 - CFCs and Halons

Estimated Global CFC Production, 1950-91

Year	Total	Propellant
	(thousand met. tons)	
1950	42	—
1951	75	—
1952	52	—
1953	65	—
1954	71	—
1955	86	—
1956	103	—
1957	110	—
1958	105	—
1959	125	—
1960	150	121
1961	170	137
1962	210	171
1963	250	195
1964	290	228
1965	330	255
1966	390	296
1967	440	333
1968	510	379
1969	530	421
1970	640	467
1971	690	492
1972	790	546
1973	900	619
1974	970	670
1975	860	480
1976	920	485
1977	880	406
1978	880	366
1979	850	317
1980	880	310
1981	890	293
1982	870	284
1983	950	293
1984	1,050	304
1985	1,090	310
1986	1,130	316
1987	1,250	321
1988	1,260	275
1989	1,150	198
1990	810	169
1991	680	125

Source: Data for 1950-59 are from Worldwatch Institute

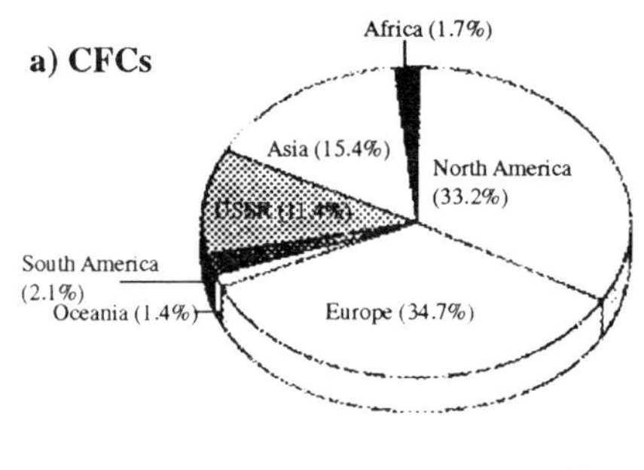

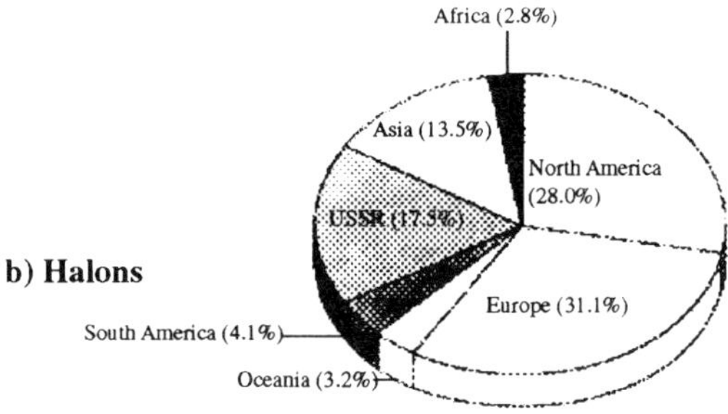

Appendix 2 - Oil Spills

Major Oil Spills – 1979-1989

Date	Tanker	Area Affected	Oil Spilled
July 1979	Atlantic Express	Tobago	276,000 tonnes
August 1983	Castello Belver	South Africa	256,000 "
March 1978	Amoco Cadiz	France	228,000 "
December 1972	Sea Star	Gulf of Oman	120,000 "
February 1980	Irenes Serenada	Greece	102,000 "
May 1976	Urquiola	Spain	101,000 "
February 1977	Hawaiian Patriot	Hawaii	99,000 "
November 1979	Independence	Turkey	95,000 "
January 1975	Jacob Maesk	Portugal	84,000 "
December 1985	Nova	Iran	71.000 "
March 1989	Exxon Valdez	Alaska	36,000 "

Source: UNEP

Appendix 3
Global Warming

Global Average Termperature, 1950-91

Year	Degrees Celsius
1950	11.87
1951	11.99
1952	12.05
1953	12.15
1954	11.94
1955	11.95
1956	11.84
1957	12.11
1958	12.11
1959	12.06
1960	12.01
1961	12.09
1962	12.03
1963	12.03
1964	11.75
1965	11.85
1966	11.92
1967	11.99
1968	11.89
1969	12.04
1970	12.05
1971	11.90
1972	11.95
1973	12.20
1974	11.94
1975	11.96
1976	11.79
1977	12.17
1978	12.10
1979	12.15
1980	12.29
1981	12.40
1982	12.08
1983	12.30
1984	12.12
1985	12.12
1986	12.17
1987	12.33
1988	12.35
1989	12.25
1990	12.47
1991	12.41

Source: NASA & UNEP

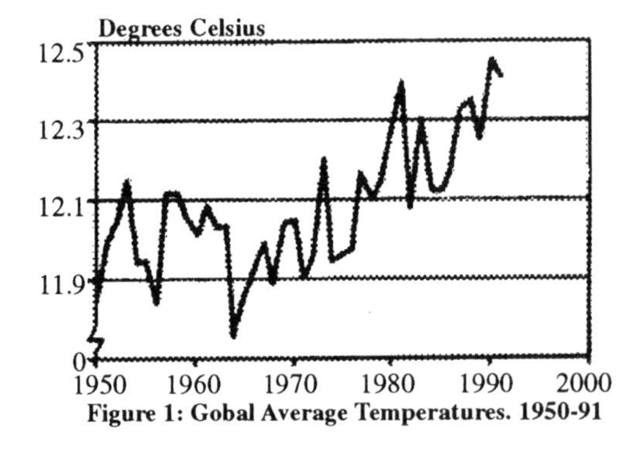

Figure 1: Gobal Average Temperatures. 1950-91

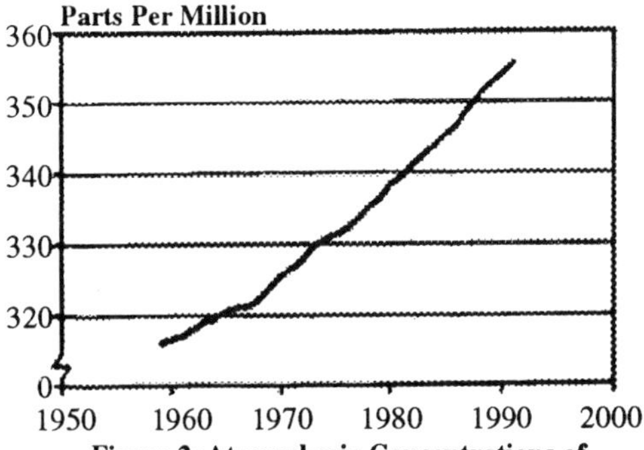

Figure 2: Atmospheric Concentrations of Carbon Dioxide, 1959-91

Appendix 4a
Carbon Emissions

World Carbon Emissions from Burning Fossil Fuels, 1950-91

Year	Emissions (*mill. met . tons*)
1950	1,620
1951	1,755
1952	1,781
1953	1,824
1954	1,844
1955	2,020
1956	2,153
1957	2,244
1958	2,302
1959	2,431
1960	2,543
1961	2,557
1962	2,659
1963	2,804
1964	2,959
1965	3,095
1966	3,251
1967	3,355
1968	3,526
1969	3,735
1970	4,013
1971	4,158
1972	4,320
1973	4,553
1974	4,560
1975	4,534
1976	4,792
1977	4,926
1978	4,966
1979	5,247
1980	5,144
1981	5,008
1982	4,973
1983	4,960
1984	5,115
1985	5,238
1986	5,415
1987	5,519
1988	5,747
1989	5,815
1990	5,830
1991 (est)	5,854

Sources: British Petroleum, UNEP

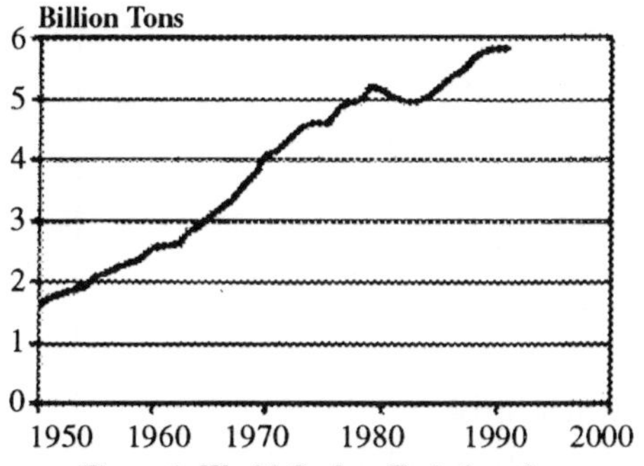

Figure 1: World Carbon Emissions from Fossil Fuel Burning, 1950-91

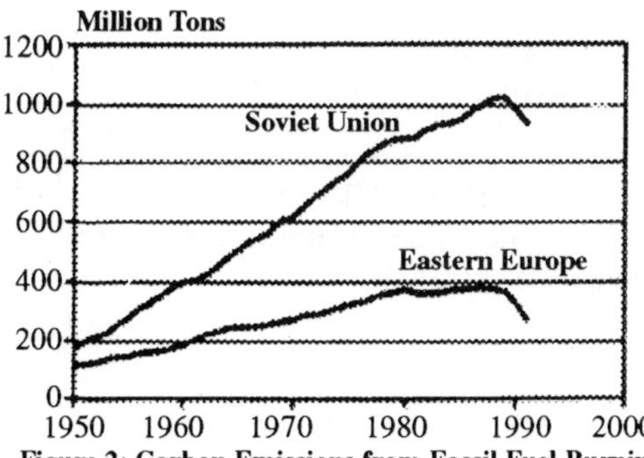

Figure 2: Carbon Emissions from Fossil Fuel Burning in Soviet Union and Eastern Europe, 1950-91

Appendix 4b
Industrial Emissions

MAJOR EMISSIONS INTO THE ATMOSPHERE FROM INDUSTRY

	million t/y	% of global anthropogenic emissions
Carbon dioxide	3,500	50
Methane	84	24
Nitrous oxide	0.2	13
Ammonia	7	20
Sulphur oxides	89	90
Nitric oxide	30	44
Particulate matter	23	40
Hydrocarbons	26	50
Chlorofluorocarbons/halons	1.2	100

Includes utilities (power stations including steam generating stations).
Chlorofluorocarbons and halons represent 1986 level (Chapter 2).
SOURCE: UNEP

Appendix 5 - Ozone Depleters

Profile of Ozone-Depleting Chemicals, 1985

Chemical	Emissions (thousand tons)	Atmospheric lifetime[1] (years)	Applications	Annual growth rate (percent)	Share of contribution to depletion[2] (percent)
CFC-12	412	139	Air conditioning, refrigeration, aerosols foams	5	45
CFC-11	238	76	Foams, aerosols, refrigeration	5	26
CFC-113	138	92	Solvents	10	12
Carbon tetrachloride	66	67	Solvents	1	8
Methyl chloroform	474	8	Solvents	7	5
Halon 1301	3	101	Fire extinguishers	n.a.	4
Halon 1211	3	12	Fire extinguishers	23	1

[1] Time it takes for 63 percent of the chemical to be washed out of the atmosphere.
[2] Total does not add to 100 due to rounding.

Source: Worldwatch Institute, Washington, D.C., December 1988.

Appendix 6 - Nuclear Power

World Electrical Generating Capacity of Nuclear Power Plants, 1950-91

Year	Capacity (*megawatts*)
1950	0
1951	0
1952	0
1953	0
1954	5
1955	5
1956	50
1957	100
1958	190
1959	380
1960	830
1961	850
1962	1,800
1963	2,100
1964	3,100
1965	4,800
1966	6,200
1967	8,300
1968	9,200
1969	13,000
1970	16,000
1971	24,000
1972	32,000
1973	45,000
1974	61,000
1975	71,000
1976	85,000
1977	59,000
1978	114,000
1979	121,000
1980	135,000
1981	155,000
1982	170,000
1983	189,000
1984	219,000
1985	250,000
1986	276,000
1987	298,000
1988	311,000
1989	321,000
1990	329,000
1991	326,000

Source: UNEP

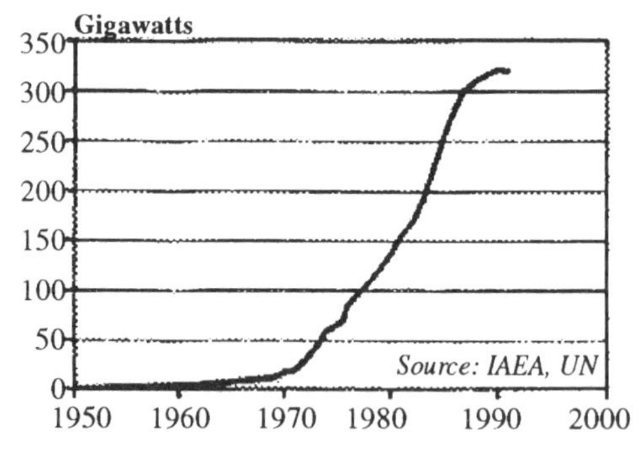

Figure 1: World Electrical Generating Capacity of Nuclear Power Plants, 1950-91.

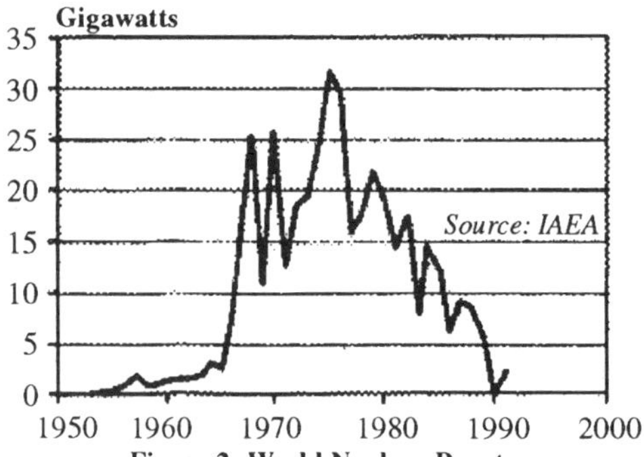

Figure 2: World Nuclear Reactor Construction Starts, 1950-91

Appendix 7 - Nuclear Weapons

GLOBAL NUCLEAR ARSENAL, 1950-91

Year	Strategic Offensive Nuclear Warheads
1950	400
1951	569
1952	660
1953	878
1954	1,418
1955	1,755
1956	2,207
1957	2,562
1958	2,836
1959	2,849
1960	3,586
1961	3,696
1962	3,928
1963	4,408
1964	5,159
1965	5,312
1966	5,801
1967	6,481
1968	6,737
1969	6,776
1970	7,431
1971	8,796
1972	10,508
1973	11,971
1974	12,514
1975	13,471
1976	14,355
1977	15,300
1978	16,856
1979	17,889
1980	18,632
1981	19,543
1982	19,977
1983	20,655
1984	21,693
1985	22,640
1986	23,133
1987	24,157
1988	24,545
1989	24,205
1990	23,718
1991	19,165

SOURCE: SIPRI Yeorbook 1992.

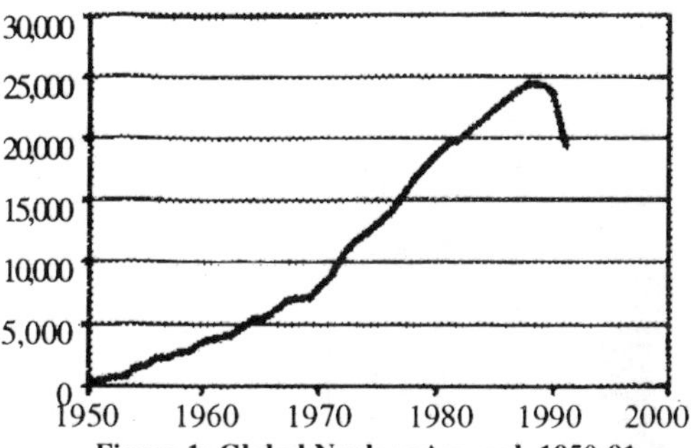

Figure 1: Global Nuclear Arsenal, 1950-91

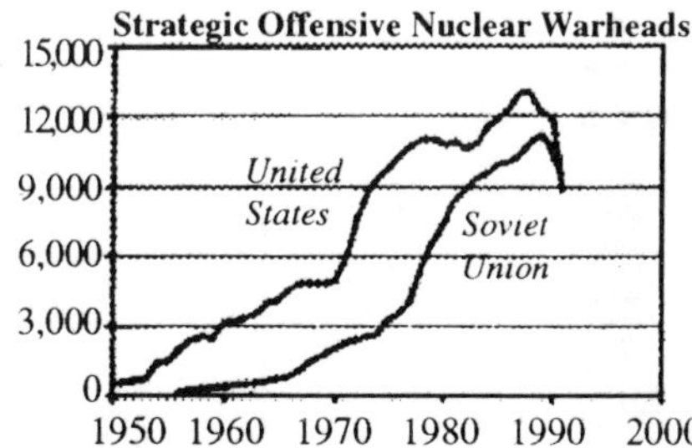

Figure 2:U.S. and Soviet Nuclear Arsenals 1950-91

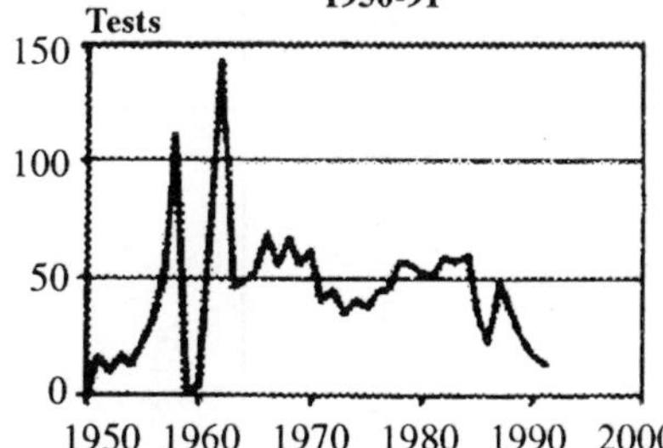

Figure 3: Nuclear Warhead Tests, 1950-91.*

* Does not reflect an additional 87 French and Soviet tests unidentified by year that took place during the period covered.

Appendix 8a - Desertification

Criteria for Estimating Degree of Desertification.

Desertification class	Plant cover	Erosion	Salinisation or waterlogging (irrigated land)	Crop yields
Slight	Excellent to good range condition class	None to slight	ECe x $10^3 < 4$ mmhos	Crop yields reduced less than 10 percent
Moderate	Fair range condition class	Moderate sheet erosion, shallow gullies, few hummocks	ECe x 10^3 4-8 mmhos	Crop yields reduced 10-50 percent
Severe	Poor range condition class	Severe sheet erosion, gullies common, occasional blow-out area	ECe x 10^3 8-15 mmhos	Crop yields reduced 50-90 percent
Very severe	Land essentially denuded of vegetation	Severely gullied, or numerous blow-out areas	Thick salt crust on nearly impermeable soils	Crop yields reduced more than 90 percent

Appendix 8b - Desertification

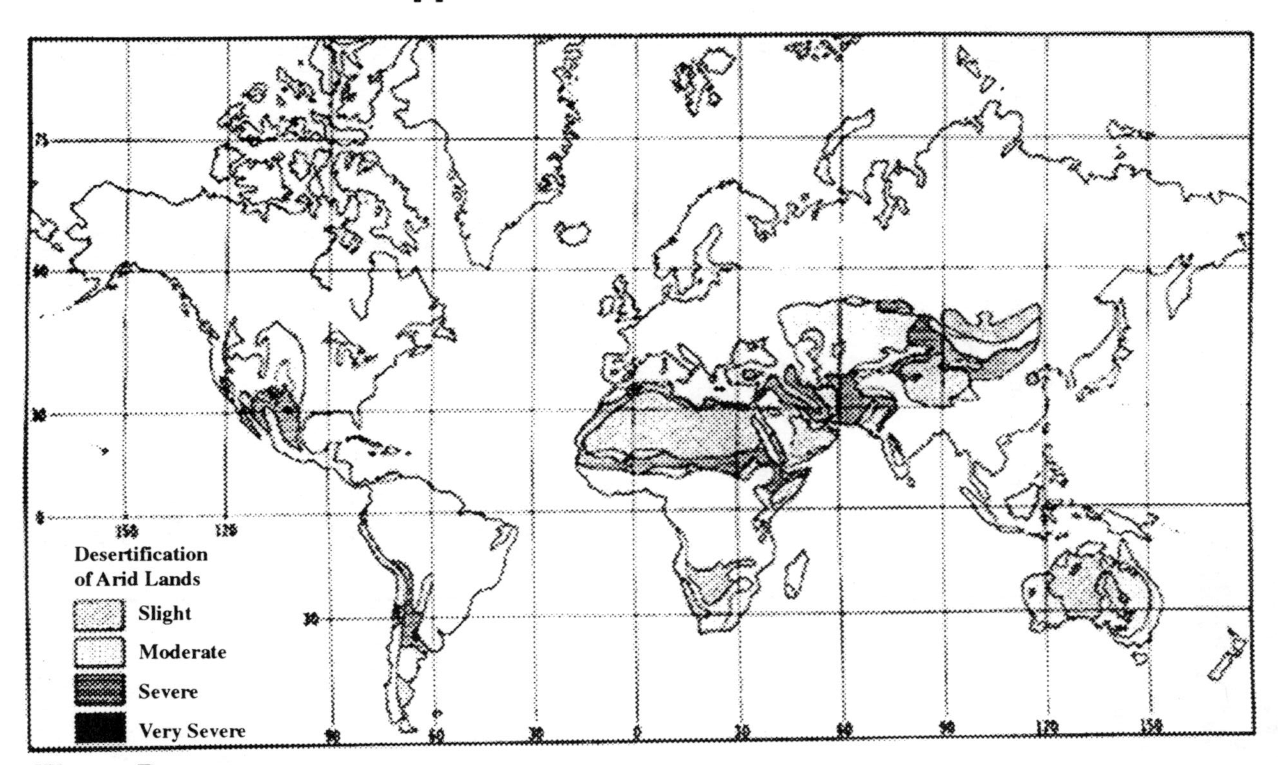

World Desertification

Appendix 8c
Desertification

Desertification of Arid Lands
Land area by continent

Continent	Desertification class	Land area, sq. km.	Percent of arid lands
Africa	Slight	12,430,000	71.7
	Moderate	1,870,000	10.8
	Severe	3,030,000	17.5
	Total	17,330,000	100.0
Asia	Slight	7,980,000	50.9
	Moderate	4,480,000	28.6
	Severe	3,210,000	20.5
	Total	15,670,000	100.0
Australia	Slight	2,330,000	36.6
	Moderate	3,510,000	55.2
	Severe	520,000	8.2
	Total	6,360,000	100.0
North America	Slight	440,000	9.9
	Moderate	2,720,000	61.5
	Severe	1,200,000	27.1
	Very severe	67,000	1.5
	Total	4,427,000	100.0
South America	Slight	1,340,000	43.6
	Moderate	1,050,000	34.1
	Severe	680,000	22.1
	Very severe	6,000	0.2
	Total	3,076,000	100.0
Europe (Spain)	Moderate	140,000	70.0
	Severe	60,000	30.0
	Total	200,000	100.0
All continents	Slight	24,520,000	52.1
	Moderate	13,770,000	29.3
	Severe	8,700,000	18.5
	Very severe	73,000	0.1
	Total	47,063,000	100.0

Source: UNEP

Appendix 9 – Automobiles

WORLD AUTOMOBILE PRODUCTION, 1950-91, in millions

Year	Production
1950	8
1951	7
1952	6
1953	8
1954	8
1955	11
1956	9
1957	10
1958	9
1959	11
1960	13
1961	11
1962	14
1963	16
1964	17
1965	19
1966	19
1967	19
1968	22
1969	23
1970	22
1971	26
1972	28
1973	30
1974	26
1975	25
1976	29
1977	30
1978	31
1979	31
1980	29
1981	28
1982	27
1983	30
1984	30
1985	32
1986	33
1987	33
1988	34
1989	36
1990	36
1991	35

SOURCE: Worldwatch Institute

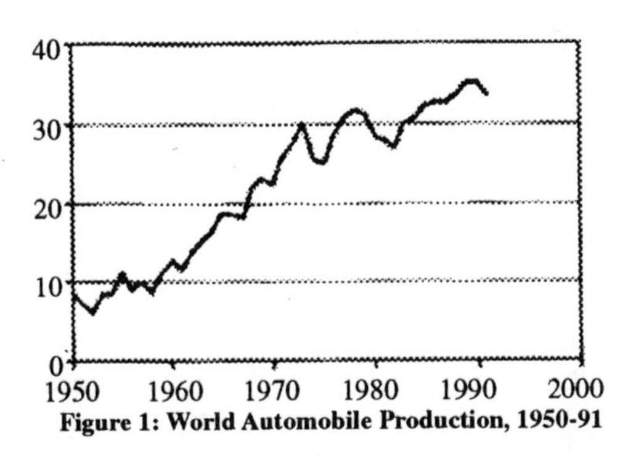

Figure 1: World Automobile Production, 1950-91

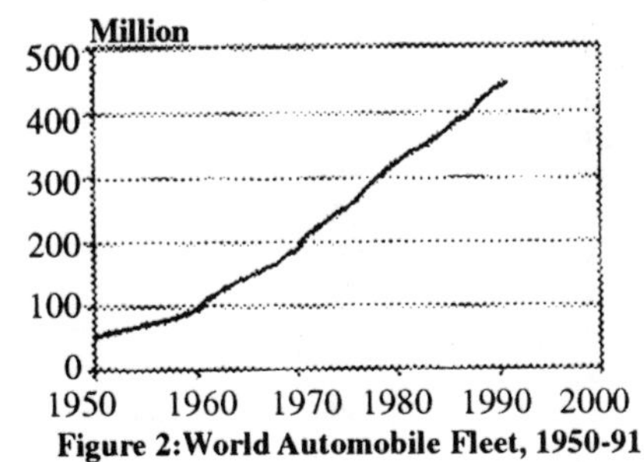

Figure 2: World Automobile Fleet, 1950-91

People
50
40
30
20
10
0
1950 1960 1970 1980 1990 2000

Figure 3: People Per Automobile, 1950-91

Appendix 10 - Arms

World Military Expenditures, 1950-90, in US dollars in billions

Year	Expenditure *(bill.1990 dollars)*
1950	230
1951	337
1952	432
1953	444
1954	399
1955	397
1956	397
1957	405
1958	399
1959	415
1960	408
1961	453
1962	495
1963	517
1964	511
1965	514
1966	561
1967	619
1968	658
1969	669
1970	658
1971	656
1972	663
1973	743
1974	766
1975	789
1976	800
1977	813
1978	837
1979	860
1980	867
1981	887
1982	940
1983	966
1984	984
1985	1,017
1986	1,021
1987	1,026
1988	1,021
1989	990
1990	934

Source: Worldwatch Institute

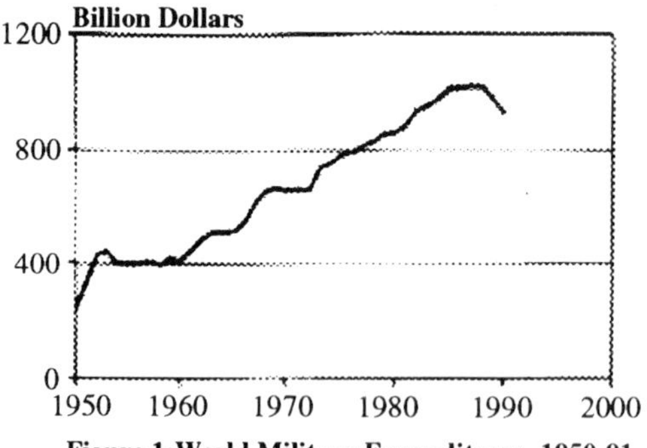

Figure 1:World Military Expenditures, 1950-91

Appendix 11 - Cigarettes

World Cigarette Production, 1950-91, in trillions

Year	Production	Per Capita
1950	1,686	657
1951	1,733	666
1952	1,780	673
1953	1,827	679
1954	1,874	684
1955	1,921	689
1956	1,968	692
1957	2,015	695
1958	2,062	698
1959	2,108	701
1960	2,150	705
1961	2,140	692
1962	2,191	696
1963	2,300	715
1964	2,402	730
1965	2,564	763
1966	2,678	781
1967	2,689	769
1968	2,790	781
1969	2,924	802
1970	3,112	836
1971	3,165	833
1972	3,295	850
1973	3,481	880
1974	3,590	890
1975	3,742	912
1976	3,852	922
1977	4,019	946
1978	4,072	942
1979	4,214	958
1980	4,388	980
1981	4,541	997
1982	4,550	982
1983	4,547	965
1984	4,689	978
1985	4,855	998
1986	4,987	1,006
1987	5,128	1 ,016
1988	5,256	1,023
1989	5,286	1,011
1990	5,414	1,018
1991	5,450	1,008

Sources: USDA, FAS, UNEP.

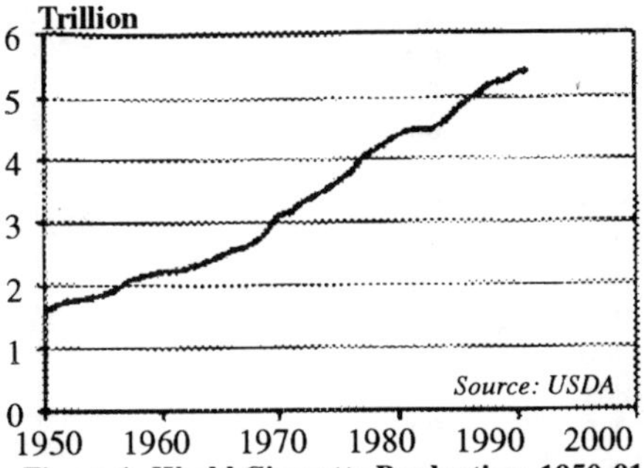

Figure 1: World Cigarette Production, 1950-91

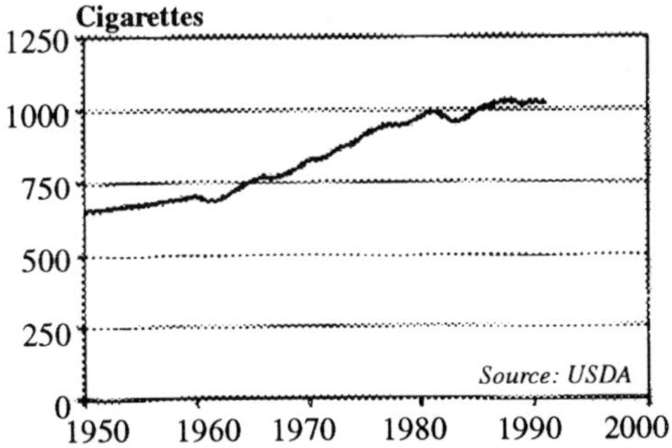

Figure 2: World Cigarette Production per Person, 1950-91

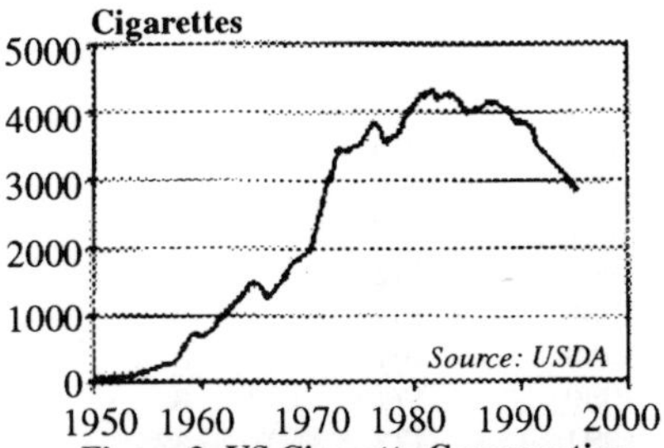

Figure 3: US Cigarette Consumption Per Person, 1950-91.

Appendix 12 - Meat

World Meat Production, 1950-91

Year	Total *(mill. met. tons)*	Per Capita *(kilograms)*
1950	46	18
1951	50	19
1952	53	20
1953	56	21
1954	58	22
1955	60	22
1956	63	22
1957	65	23
1958	67	23
1959	69	23
1960	68	22
1961	70	23
1962	73	23
1963	77	24
1964	78	24
1965	82	25
1966	86	25
1967	90	26
1968	93	26
1969	94	26
1970	98	26
1971	102	27
1972	105	27
1973	106	27
1974	112	28
1975	113	28
1976	116	28
1977	120	28
1978	125	29
1979	129	30
1980	133	30
1981	136	30
1982	137	30
1983	142	30
1984	145	30
1985	150	31
1986	156	32
1987	161	32
1988	164	32
1989	167	32
1990	171	32
1991	173	32

Source: FAO (Rome)

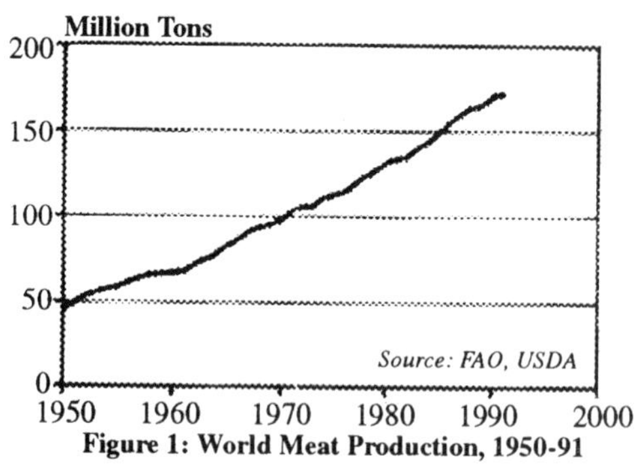

Figure 1: World Meat Production, 1950-91

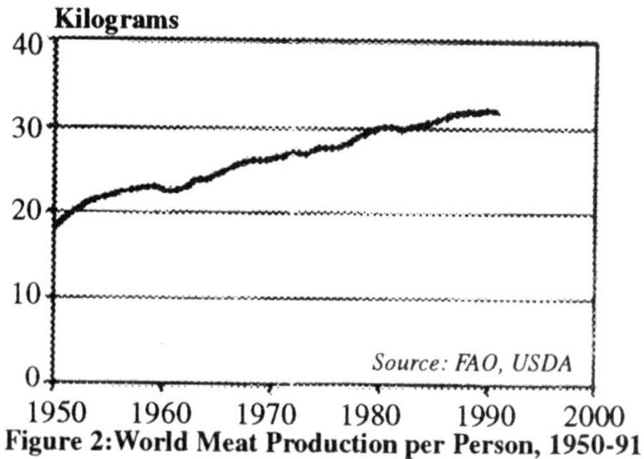

Figure 2: World Meat Production per Person, 1950-91

Figure 3: World Meat Production By Type, 1950-91.

Appendix 13 - Fish

World Fish Catch, 1950—90

Year	**Total** *(mill. met. tons)*	**Per Capita** *(kilograms)*
1950	22	9
1951	26	10
1952	25	10
1953	26	10
1954	27	10
1955	29	10
1956	30	11
1957	31	11
1958	33	11
1959	36	12
1960	38	12
1961	42	14
1962	45	14
1963	48	15
1964	53	16
1965	54	16
1966	57	17
1967	60	17
1968	64	18
1969	63	17
1970	66	18
1971	66	17
1972	62	16
1973	63	16
1974	67	16
1975	66	16
1976	69	17
1977	70	16
1978	70	16
1979	71	16
1980	72	16
1981	75	16
1982	77	17
1983	78	16
1984	84	17
1985	86	18
1986	92	19
1987	93	18
1988	99	19
1989	100	19
1990 (est)	97	18

Source: FAO (Rome)

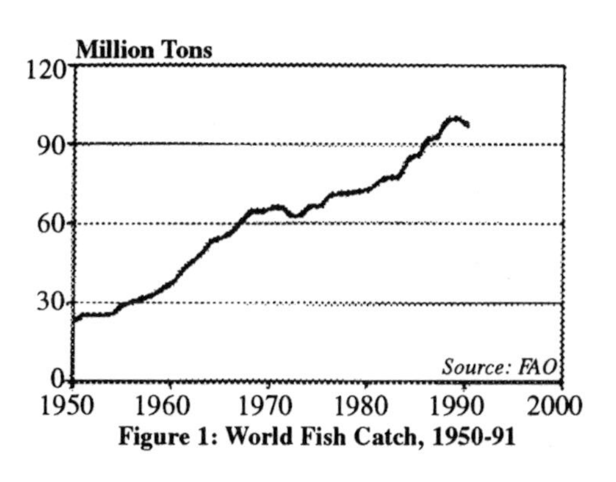

Figure 1: World Fish Catch, 1950-91

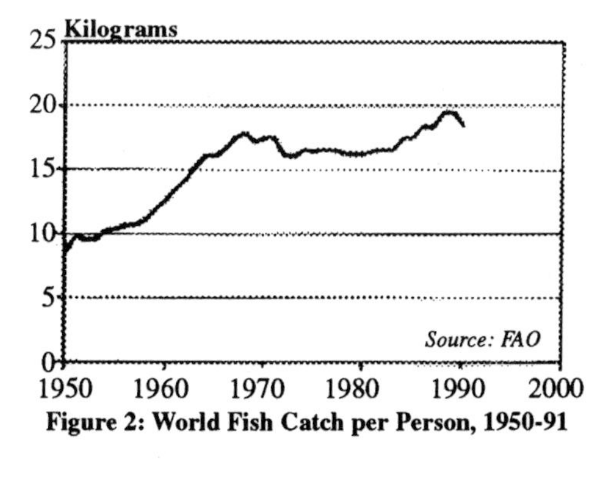

Figure 2: World Fish Catch per Person, 1950-91